THE OUTER LIMITS™

VOLUME

TWO

Also available

The Outer Limits, Volume One

with stories by

HARLAN ELLISON
DIANE DUANE
JOHN M. FORD
HOWARD V. HENDRIX

THE OUTER LIMITS

V O L U M E

TWO

Edited by
Debbie Notkin

BOXTREE

First published in 1997 in the USA by Prima Publishing,
Prima Communications, Inc.
Authorized reprint from US edition.

This edition published in 1997 by Boxtree, an imprint of Macmillan
Publishers Ltd, 28 Eccleston Place, London, SW1W 9NF and Basingstoke

Associated companies throughout the world

ISBN 0 7522 0279 0

9 8 7 6 5 4 3 2 1

A CIP catalogue record for this book is available from the British Library

Printed by Mackays of Chatham plc, Chatham, Kent

*To Beth Meacham, who opened a
door that I thought had closed forever.*

Contents

Introduction

If you think about it, *The Outer Limits* (and its major competition, *The Twilight Zone*) were the pioneers of horror and science fiction TV. *The Outer Limits* brought horror, which had previously been the fodder of Roger Corman movies and paperback novels, to the small screen—in a big way.

Today, when *Star Trek* is a household word, when *The X-Files* dominates television ratings, when everyone is discussing whether or not *Millennium* goes too far, it's hard to remember what a change from the television fare of the time *The Outer Limits* really was. In a market otherwise saturated by the sitcoms that now grace "Nick at Nite," where drama was *Dr. Kildare* and scary drama was *The Man from U.N.C.L.E.*, when most people had never seen anything scarier than *The Wizard of Oz* on their TV screens, *The Outer Limits* was far more daring than *Millennium* is today.

As for themes and topics, the sky was not the limit, it was barely the starting place. Look at "A Feasibility Study" in this volume. In the late 1960s, this show offered a highly charged sex scene (while Dick van Dyke and Mary Tyler Moore were still sleeping in twin beds), made a clear reference to the Holocaust, and ended with a stirring examination of the nature of true sacrifice—without ever losing its thread about the *Dilbert*-ization of American business (come to think of it, Scott Adams was probably a ten year old watching the show—maybe *this* is where he got his first ideas).

Thanks to MGM/UA, the 1990s *Outer Limits* series follows that lead, making people think, pushing boundaries, taking risks. And it's being rewarded: the series' second CableACE Award was handed out in November 1996. These print anthologies bring the whole show, old series and new, into your bookstore and into your hands, with retellings by familiar authors like Diane Duane and Richard Lupoff, plus newcomer Michael Marano, and as a bonus, classic SF author Fredric Brown's most famous story.

So, sit back and relax. There's no need to adjust the print on these pages. . . . We control the typeface. . . . We control the margins. . . .

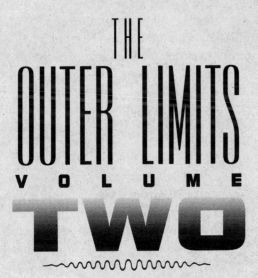

"Arena," first published in 1944, combines two irresistible stories. Everyone likes a good battle story . . . and every science fiction reader likes a good cross-cultural story. Here they are, both in one package. If you remember the old Outer Limits *episode "Fun and Games," you may find this quite familiar.*

Arena

Fredric Brown

CARSON OPENED his eyes, and found himself looking upward into a flickering blue dimness.

It was hot, and he was lying on sand, and a sharp rock embedded in the sand was hurting his back. He rolled over to his side, off the rock, and then pushed himself up to a sitting position.

"I'm crazy," he thought. "Crazy—or dead—or something." The sand was blue, bright blue. And there wasn't any such thing as bright blue sand on Earth or any of the planets.

Blue sand.

Blue sand under a blue dome that wasn't the sky nor yet a room, but a circumscribed area—somehow he knew it was circumscribed and finite even though he couldn't see to the top of it.

He picked up some of the sand in his hand and let it run through his fingers. It trickled down onto his bare leg. *Bare?*

Naked. He was stark naked, and already his body was dripping perspiration from the enervating heat, coated blue with sand wherever sand had touched it.

But elsewhere his body was white.

He thought: Then this sand is really blue. If it seemed blue only because of the blue light, then I'd be blue also. But I'm white, so the sand *is* blue. Blue *sand*. There isn't any blue sand. There isn't any place like this place I'm in.

Sweat was running down in his eyes.

It was hot, hotter than hell. Only hell—the hell of the ancients—was supposed to be red and not blue.

But if this place wasn't hell, what was it? Only Mercury, among the planets, had heat like this and this wasn't Mercury. And Mercury was some four billion miles from—

It came back to him then, where he'd been. In the little one-man scouter, outside the orbit of Pluto, scouting a scant million miles to one side of the Earth Armada drawn up in battle array there to intercept the Outsiders.

That sudden strident nerve-shattering ringing of the alarm bell when the rival scouter—the Outsider ship—had come within range of his detectors—

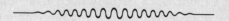

No one knew who the outsiders were, what they looked like, from what far galaxy they came, other than that it was in the general direction of the Pleiades.

First, sporadic raids on Earth colonies and outposts. Isolated battles between Earth patrols and small groups of Outsider spaceships; battles sometimes won and sometimes lost, but never to date resulting in the capture of an alien vessel. Nor had any member of a raided colony ever survived to describe the Outsiders who had left the ships, if indeed they had left them.

Not a too-serious menace, at first, for the raids had not been too numerous or destructive. And individually, the ships had proved slightly inferior in armament to the best of Earth's fighters, although somewhat superior in speed and maneuverability. A sufficient edge in speed, in fact, to give the Outsiders their choice of running or fighting, unless surrounded.

Nevertheless, Earth had prepared for serious trouble, for a showdown, building the mightiest armada of all time. It had been waiting now, that armada, for a long time. But now the showdown was coming.

Scouts twenty billion miles out had detected the approach of a mighty fleet—a showdown fleet—of the Outsiders. Those scouts had never come back, but their radiotronic messages had. And now Earth's armada, all ten thousand ships and half-million fighting spacemen, was out there, outside Pluto's orbit, waiting to intercept and battle to the death.

And an even battle it was going to be, judging by the advance reports of the men of the far picket line who had given their lives to report—before they had died—on the size and strength of the alien fleet.

Anybody's battle, with the mastery of the solar system hanging in the balance, on an even chance. A last and *only* chance, for Earth and all her colonies lay at the utter mercy of the Outsiders if they ran that gauntlet—

Oh yes. Bob Carson remembered now.

Not that it explained blue sand and flickering blueness. But that strident alarming of the bell and his leap for the control panel. His frenzied fumbling as he strapped himself into the seat. The dot in the visiplate that grew larger.

The dryness of his mouth. The awful knowledge that this was *it*. For him, at least, although the main fleets were still out of range of one another.

This, his first taste of battle. Within three seconds or less he'd be victorious, or a charred cinder. Dead.

Three seconds—that's how long a space-battle lasted. Time enough to count to three, slowly, and then you'd won or you were dead. One hit completely took care of a lightly armed and armored little one-man craft like a scouter.

Frantically—as, unconsciously, his dry lips shaped the word "One"—he worked at the controls to keep that growing dot centered on the crossed spiderwebs of the visiplate. His hands doing that, while his right foot hovered over the pedal that would fire the bolt. The single bolt of concentrated hell that had to hit— or else. There wouldn't be time for any second shot.

"Two." He didn't know he'd said that, either. The dot in the visiplate wasn't a dot now. Only a few thousand miles away, it showed up in the magnification of the plate as though it were only a few hundred yards off. It was a sleek, fast little scouter, about the size of his.

And an alien ship, all right.

"Thr—" His foot touched the bolt-release pedal—

And then the Outsider had swerved suddenly and was off the cross-hairs. Carson punched the keys frantically, to follow.

For a tenth of a second, it was out of the visiplate entirely, and then as the nose of his scouter swung after it, he saw it again, diving straight toward the ground.

The ground?

It was an optical illusion of the same sort. It *had* to be, that planet—or whatever it was—that now covered the visiplate. Whatever it was, it couldn't be there. Couldn't possibly. There *wasn't* any planet nearer than Neptune three billion miles away—with Pluto around on the opposite side of the distant pinpoint sun.

His *detectors! They* hadn't shown any object of planetary dimensions, even of asteroid dimensions. They still didn't.

So it couldn't be there, that whatever-it-was he was diving into, only a few hundred miles below him.

And in his sudden anxiety to keep from crashing, he forgot even the Outsider ship. He fired the front braking rockets, and even as the sudden change of speed slammed him forward against the seat straps, he fired full right for an emergency turn. Pushed them down and *held* them down, knowing that he needed everything the ship had to keep from crashing and that a turn that sudden would black him out for a moment.

It did black him out.

And that was all. Now he was sitting in hot blue sand, stark naked but otherwise unhurt. No sign of his spaceship and—for that matter—no sign of *space.* That curve overhead wasn't a sky, whatever else it was.

He scrambled to his feet.

Gravity seemed a little bit more than Earth-normal. Not much more.

Flat sand stretching away, a few scrawny bushes in clumps here and there. The bushes were blue, too, but in varying shades, some lighter than the blue of the sand, some darker.

Out from under the nearest bush ran a little thing that was like a lizard, except that it had more than four legs. It was blue, too. Bright blue. It saw him and ran back again under the bush.

He looked up again, trying to decide what was overhead. It wasn't exactly a roof, but it was dome-shaped. It flickered and was hard to look at. But definitely, it curved down to the ground, to the blue sand, all around him.

He wasn't far from being under the center of the dome. At a guess, it was a hundred yards to the nearest wall, if it was a wall. It was as though a blue hemisphere of *something,* about two hundred and fifty yards in circumference, was inverted over the flat expanse of the sand.

And everything blue, except one object. Over near a far curving wall there was a red object. Roughly spherical, it seemed to be about a yard in diameter. Too far for him to see clearly through the flickering blueness. But, unaccountably, he shuddered.

He wiped sweat from his forehead, or tried to, with the back of his hand.

Was this a dream, a nightmare? This heat, this sand, that vague feeling of horror he felt when he looked toward the red thing?

A dream? No, one didn't go to sleep and dream in the midst of a battle in space.

Death? No, never. If there were immortality, it wouldn't be a senseless thing like this, a thing of blue heat and blue sand and red horror.

Then he heard the voice—

Inside his head he heard it, not with his ears. It came from nowhere or everywhere.

"Through spaces and dimensions wandering," rang the words in his mind, *"and in this space and this time I find two people about to wage a war that would exterminate one and so weaken the other that it would retrogress and never fulfill its destiny, but decay and return to mindless dust whence it came. And I say this must not happen."*

"Who . . . what are you?" Carson didn't say it aloud, but the question formed itself in his brain.

"You would not understand completely. I am—" There was pause as though the voice sought—in Carson's brain—for a word that wasn't there, a word he didn't know. *"I am the end of evolution of a race so old*

the time can not be expressed in words that have meaning to your mind. A race fused into a single entity, eternal—

"*An entity such as your primitive race might become*"—again the groping for a word—"*time from now. So might the race you call, in your mind, the Outsiders. So I intervene in the battle to come, the battle between fleets so evenly matched that destruciton of both races will result. One must survive. One must progress and evolve.*"

"One?" thought Carson. "Mine, or—?"

"*It is in my power to stop the war, to send the Outsiders back to their galaxy. But they would return, or your race would sooner or later follow them there. Only by remaining in this space and time to intervene constantly could I prevent them from destroying one another, and I cannot remain.*

"*So I shall intervene now. I shall destroy one fleet completely without loss to the other. One civilization shall thus survive.*"

Nightmare. This had to be a nightmare, Carson thought. But he knew it wasn't.

It was too mad, too impossible, to be anything but real.

He didn't dare ask *the* question—*which?* But his thoughts asked it for him.

"*The stronger shall survive,*" said the voice. "*That I can not—and would not—change. I merely intervene to make it a complete victory, not*"—groping again—"*not Pyrrhic victory to a broken race.*

"*From the outskirts of the not-yet battle I plucked two individuals, you and an Outsider. I see from your mind that in your early history of nationalisms battles between champions, to decide between races, were not unknown.*

"*You and your opponent are here pitted against one another, naked and unarmed, under conditions equally unfamiliar to you both, equally unpleasant to you both. There is no time limit, for here there is no time. The survivor is the champion of his race. That race survives.*"

"But—" Carson's protest was too inarticulate for expression, but the voice answered it.

"*It is fair. The conditions are such that the accident of physical strength will not completely decide the issue. There is a barrier. You will understand. Brain-power and courage will be more important than strength. Most especially courage, which is the will to survive.*"

"But while this goes on, the fleets will—"

"*No, you are in another space, another time. For as long as you are here, time stands still in the universe you know. I see you wonder whether this place is real. It is, and it is not. As I—to your limited understanding—am and am not real. My existence is mental and not physical. You saw me as a planet; it could have been as a dustmote or a sun.*

"*But to you this place is now real. What you suffer here will be real. And if you die here, your death will be real. If you die, your failure will be the end of your race. That is enough for you to know.*"

And then the voice was gone.

And he was alone, but not alone. For as Carson looked up, he saw that the red thing, the red sphere of horror which he now knew was the Outsider, was rolling toward him.

Rolling.

It seemed to have no legs or arms that he could see, no features. It rolled across the blue sand with the fluid quickness of a drop of mercury. And before it, in some manner he could not understand, came a paralyzing wave of nauseating, retching, horrid hatred.

Carson looked about him frantically. A stone, lying in the sand a few feet away, was the nearest thing to a weapon. It wasn't large, but it had sharp edges, like a slab of flint. It looked a bit like blue flint.

He picked it up, and crouched to receive the attack. It was coming fast, faster than he could run.

No time to think out how he was going to fight it, and how anyway could he plan to battle a creature whose strength, whose characteristics, whose method of fighting he did not know? Rolling so fast, it looked more than ever like a perfect sphere.

Ten yards away. Five. And then it stopped.

Rather, it *was stopped*. Abruptly the near side of it flattened as though it had run up against an invisible wall. It bounced, actually bounced back.

Then it rolled forward again, but more slowly, more cautiously. It stopped again, at the same place. It tried again, a few yards to one side.

There was a barrier there of some sort. It clicked, then, in Carson's mind. That thought projected into his mind by the Entity who had brought them there: "—accident of physical strength will not completely decide the issue. There is a barrier."

A force-field, of course. Not the Netzian Field, known to Earth science, for that glowed and emitted a crackling sound. This one was invisible, silent.

It was a wall that ran from side to side of the inverted hemisphere; Carson didn't have to verify that himself. The Roller was doing that; rolling sideways along the barrier, seeking a break in it that wasn't there.

Carson took half a dozen steps forward, his left hand groping out before him, and then his hand touched the barrier. It felt smooth, yielding, like a sheet of rubber rather than like glass. Warm to his touch, but no warmer than the sand underfoot. And it was completely invisible, even at close range.

He dropped the stone and put both hands against it, pushing. It seemed to yield, just a trifle. But no farther than that trifle, even when he pushed with all his weight. It felt like a sheet of rubber backed up by steel. Limited resiliency, and then firm strength.

He stood on tiptoe and reached as high as he could and the barrier was still there.

He saw the Roller coming back, having reached one side of the arena. That feeling of nausea hit Carson again, and he stepped back from the barrier as it went by. It didn't stop.

But did the barrier stop at ground level? Carson knelt down and burrowed in the sand. It was soft, light, easy to dig in. At two feet down the barrier was still there.

The Roller was coming back again. Obviously, it couldn't find a way through at either side.

There must be a way through, Carson thought. *Some* way we can get at each other, else this duel is meaningless.

But no hurry now, in finding that out. There was something to try first. The Roller was back now, and it stopped just across the barrier, only six feet away. It seemed to be studying him, although for the life of him, Carson couldn't find external evidence of sense organs on the thing. Nothing that looked like eyes or ears, or even a mouth. There was though, he saw now, a series of grooves—perhaps a dozen of them altogether, and he saw two tentacles suddenly push out from two of the grooves and dip into the sand as though testing its consistency. Tentacles about an inch in diameter and perhaps a foot and a half long.

But the tentacles were retractable into the grooves and were kept there except when in use. They were retractable when the thing rolled and seemed to have nothing to do with its method of locomotion. That, as far as Carson could judge, seemed to be accomplished by some shifting—just *how* he couldn't even imagine—of its center of gravity.

He shuddered as he looked at the thing. It was alien, utterly alien, horribly different from anything on Earth or any of the life forms found on the other solar planets. Instinctively, somehow, he knew its mind was as alien as its body.

But he had to try. If it had no telepathic powers at all, the attempt was foredoomed to failure, yet he thought it had such powers. There had, at any rate, been a projection of something that was not physical at the time a few minutes ago when it had first started for him. An almost tangible wave of hatred.

If it could project that, perhaps it could read his mind as well, sufficiently for his purpose.

Deliberately, Carson picked up the rock that had been his only weapon, then tossed it down again in a gesture of relinquishment and raised his empty hands, palms up, before him.

He spoke aloud, knowing that although the words would be meaningless to the creature before him, speaking them would focus his own thoughts more completely upon the message.

"Can we not have peace between us?" he said, his voice sounding strange in the utter stillness. "The Entity who brought us here has told us what must happen if our races fight—extinction of one and weakening and retrogression of the other. The battle between them, said the Entity, depends upon what we do here. Why can not we agree to an external peace—your race to its galaxy, we to ours?"

Carson blanked out his mind to receive a reply.

It came, and staggered him back, physically. He actually recoiled several steps in sheer horror at the depth and intensity of the hatred and lust-to-kill of the red images that had been projected at him. Not as articulate words—as had come to him the thoughts of the Entity—but as wave upon wave of fierce emotion.

For a moment that seemed an eternity he had to struggle against the mental impact of that hatred, fight to clear his mind of it and drive out the alien thoughts to which he had given admittance by blanking out his own thoughts. He wanted to retch.

Slowly his mind cleared as, slowly, the mind of a man wakening from nightmare clears away the fear-fabric of which the dream was woven. He was breathing hard and he felt weaker, but he could think.

He stood studying the Roller. It had been motionless during the mental duel it had so nearly won. Now it rolled a few feet to one side, to the nearest of the blue bushes. Three tentacles whipped out of their grooves and began to investigate the bush.

"O.K.," Carson said, "so it's war then." He managed a wry grin. "If I got your answer straight, peace doesn't appeal to you." And, because he was, after all, a quiet young man and couldn't resist the impulse to be dramatic, he added, "To the death!"

But his voice, in that utter silence, sounded very silly, even to himself. It came to him, then, that this *was* to the death. Not only his own death or that of the red spherical thing which he now thought of as the Roller, but death to the entire race of one or the other of them. The end of the human race, if he failed.

It made him suddenly very humble and very afraid to think that. More than to think it, to *know* it. Somehow, with a knowledge that was above even faith, he knew that the Entity who had arranged this duel had told the truth about its intentions and its powers. It wasn't kidding.

The future of humanity depended upon *him*. It was an awful thing to realize, and he wrenched his mind away from it. He had to concentrate on the situation at hand.

There had to be some way of getting through the barrier, or of killing through the barrier.

Mentally? He hoped that wasn't all, for the Roller obviously had stronger telepathic powers than the primitive, undeveloped ones of the human race. Or did it?

He had been able to drive the thoughts of the Roller out of his own mind; could it drive out his? If its ability to project were stronger, might not its receptivity mechanism be more vulnerable?

He stared at it and endeavored to concentrate and focus all his thoughts upon it.

"Die," he thought. *"You are going to die. You are dying. You are—"* He tried variations on it, and mental pictures. Sweat stood out on his forehead and he found himself trembling with the intensity of the effort. But the Roller went ahead with its investigation of the bush, as utterly unaffected as though Carson had been reciting the multiplication table.

So *that* was no good.

He felt a bit weak and dizzy from the heat and his strenuous effort at concentration. He sat down on the blue sand to rest and gave his full attention to watching and studying the Roller. By close study, perhaps, he could judge its strengths and detect its weaknesses, learn things that would be valuable to know when and if they should come to grips.

It was breaking off twigs. Carson watched carefully, trying to judge just how hard it worked to do that. Later, he thought, he could find a similar bush on his own side, break off twigs of equal thickness himself, and gain a comparison of physical strength between his own arms and hands and those tentacles.

The twigs broke off hard; the Roller was having to struggle with each one, he saw. Each tentacle, he saw, bifurcated at the tip into two fingers, each tipped by a nail or claw. The claws didn't seem to be particularly long or dangerous. No more so than his own fingernails, if they were let to grow a bit.

No, on the whole, it didn't look too tough to handle physically. Unless, of course, that bush was made of pretty tough stuff. Carson looked around him and, yes, right within reach was another bush of identical type.

He reached over and snapped off a twig. It was brittle, easy to break. Of course, the Roller might have been faking deliberately but he didn't think so.

On the other hand, where was it vulnerable? Just how would he go about killing it, if he got the chance? He went back to studying it. The outer hide looked pretty tough. He'd need a sharp weapon of some sort. He picked up the piece of rock again. It was about twelve inches long, narrow, and fairly sharp on one end. If it chipped like flint, he could make a serviceable knife out of it.

The Roller was continuing its investigations of the bushes. It rolled again, to the nearest one of another type. A little blue lizard, many-legged like the one Carson had seen on his side of the barrier, darted out from under the bush.

A tentacle of the Roller lashed out and caught it, picked it up. Another tentacle whipped over and began to pull legs off the lizard, as coldly and calmly as it had pulled twigs off the bush. The creature struggled frantically and emitted a shrill squealing sound that was the first sound Carson had heard here other than the sound of his own voice.

Carson shuddered and wanted to turn his eyes away. But he made himself continue to watch; anything he could learn about his opponent might prove valuable. Even this knowledge of its unnecessary cruelty. Particularly, he thought with a sudden vicious surge of emotion, this knowledge of its unnecessary cruelty. It would make it a pleasure to kill the thing, if and when the chance came.

He steeled himself to watch the dismembering of the lizard, for that very reason.

But he felt glad when, with half its legs gone, the lizard quit squealing and struggling and lay limp and dead in the Roller's grasp.

It didn't continue with the rest of the legs. Contemptuously it tossed the dead lizard away from it, in Carson's direction. It arced through the air between them and landed at his feet.

It had come through the barrier! The barrier wasn't there anymore!

Carson was on his feet in a flash, the knife gripped tightly in his hand, and leaped forward. He'd settle this thing here and now! With the barrier gone—

But it wasn't gone. He had found that out the hard way, running head-on into it and nearly knocking himself silly. He bounced back, and fell.

And as he sat up, shaking his head to clear it, he saw something coming through the air toward him, and to duck it, he threw himself flat again on the sand, and to one side. He got his body out of the way, but there was a sudden sharp pain in the calf of his left leg.

He rolled backward, ignoring the pain, and scrambled to his feet. It was a rock, he saw now, that had struck him. And the Roller was picking up another one now, swinging it back gripped between two tentacles, getting ready to throw again.

It sailed through the air toward him, but he was easily able to step out of its way. The Roller, apparently, could throw straight, but not hard nor far. The first rock had struck him only because he had been sitting down and had not seen it coming until it was almost upon him.

Even as he stepped aside from that weak second throw, Carson drew back his right arm and let fly with the rock that was still in his hand. If missiles, he thought with sudden elation, can cross the barrier, then two can play at the game of throwing them. And the good right arm of an Earthman—

He couldn't miss a three-foot sphere at only four-yard range, and he didn't miss. The rock whizzed straight, and with a speed several times that of the missiles the Roller had thrown. It hit dead center, but it hit flat, unfortunately, instead of point first.

But it hit with such a resounding thump, and obviously it hurt. The Roller had been reaching for another rock, but it changed its mind and got out of there instead. By the time Carson could pick up another rock, the Roller was forty yards back from the barrier and going strong.

His second throw missed by feet, and his third throw was short. The Roller was back out of range— at least out of range of a missile heavy enough to be damaging.

Carson grinned. That round had been his. Except—

He quit grinning as he bent over to examine the calf of his leg. A jagged edge of the stone had made a pretty deep cut, several inches long. It was bleeding pretty freely, but he didn't think it had gone deep enough to hit an artery. If it stopped bleeding of its own accord, well and good. If not, he was in for trouble.

Finding out one thing, though, took precedence over that cut. The nature of the barrier.

He went forward to it again, this time groping with his hands before him. He found it; then holding one hand against it, he tossed a handful of sand at it with the other hand. The sand went right through. His hand didn't.

Organic matter versus inorganic? No, because the dead lizard had gone through it, and a lizard, dead or alive, was certainly organic. Plant life? He broke off a twig and poked at the barrier. The twig went through, with no resistance, but when his fingers gripping the twig came to the barrier, they were stopped.

He couldn't get through it, nor could the Roller. But the rocks and sand and a dead lizard—

How about a live lizard? He went hunting, under bushes, until he found one, and caught it. He tossed it gently against the barrier and it bounced back and scurried away across the blue sand.

That gave him the answer, insofar as he could determine it now. The screen was a barrier to living things. Dead or inorganic matter could cross it.

That off his mind, Carson looked at his injured leg again. The bleeding was lessening, which meant he wouldn't need to worry about making a tourniquet. But he should find some water, if any was available, to clean the wound.

Water—the thought made him realize that he was getting awfully thirsty. He'd *have* to find water, in case this contest turned out to be a protracted one.

Limping slightly now, he started off to make a full curcuit of his half of the arena. Guiding himself with one hand along the barrier, he walked to his right until he came to the curving sidewall. It was visible, a dull blue-grey at close range, and the surface of it felt just like the central barrier.

He experimented by tossing a handful of sand at it, and the sand reached the wall and disappeared as it went through. The hemispherical shell was a force-field, too. But an opaque one, instead of transparent like the barrier.

He followed it around until he came back to the barrier, and walked back along the barrier to the point from which he'd started.

No sign of water.

Worried now, he started a series of zigzags back and forth between the barrier and the wall, covering the intervening space thoroughly.

No water. Blue sand, blue bushes, and intolerable heat. Nothing else.

It must be his imagination, he told himself angrily, that he was suffering *that* much from thirst. How long had he been here? Of course, no time at all, according to his own spacetime frame. The Entity had told him time stood still out there, while he was here. But his body processes went on here, just the same. And according to his body's reckoning, how long had he been here? Three or four hours, perhaps. Certainly not long enough to be suffering seriously from thirst.

But he was suffering from it; his throat dry and parched. Probably the intense heat was the cause. It was *hot!* A hundred and thirty Fahrenheit, at a guess. A dry, still heat without the slightest movement of air.

He was limping rather badly, and utterly fagged out when he'd finished the futile exploration of his domain.

He stared across at the motionless Roller and hoped it was as miserable as he was. And quite possibly it wasn't enjoying this, either. The Entity had said the conditions here were equally unfamiliar and equally uncomfortable for both of them. Maybe the Roller came from a planet where two-hundred-degree heat was the norm. Maybe it was freezing while he was roasting.

Maybe the air was as much too thick for it as it was too thin for him. For the exertion of his explorations had left him panting. The atmosphere here, he realized now, was not much thicker than that on Mars.

No water.

That meant a deadline, for him at any rate. Unless he could find a way to cross that barrier or to kill his enemy from this side of it, thirst would kill him eventually.

It gave him a feeling of desperate urgency. He *must* hurry.

But he made himself sit down for a moment to rest, to think.

What was there to do? Nothing and yet so many things. The several varieties of bushes, for example. They didn't look promising, but he'd have to examine them for possibilities. And his leg—he'd have to do something about that, even without water to clean it. Gather ammunition in the form of rocks. Find a rock that would make a good knife.

His leg hurt rather badly now, and he decided that came first. One type of bush had leaves—or things rather similar to leaves. He pulled off a handful of them and decided, after examination, to take a chance on them. He used them to clean off the sand and dirt and caked blood, then made a pad of fresh leaves and tied it over the wound with tendrils from the same bush.

The tendrils proved unexpectedly tough and strong. They were slender, and soft and pliable, yet he couldn't break them at all. He had to saw them off the bush with the sharp edge of a piece of the blue flint. Some of the thicker ones were over a foot long, and he filed away in his memory, for future reference, the fact that a bunch of the thick ones, tied together, would make a pretty serviceable rope. Maybe he'd be able to think of a use for rope.

Next he made himself a knife. The blue flint *did* chip. From a foot-long splinter of it, he fashioned himself a crude but lethal weapon. And of tendrils from the bush, he made himself a rope-belt through which he could thrust the flint knife, to keep it with him all the time and yet have his hands free.

He went back to studying the bushes. There were three other types. One was leafless, dry, brittle, rather like a dried tumbleweed. Another was of soft, crumbly wood, almost like punk. It looked and felt as though it would make excellent tinder for fire. The third type was the most nearly woodlike. It had fragile leaves that wilted at a touch, but the stalks, although short, were straight and strong.

It was horribly, unbearably hot.

He limped up to the barrier, felt to make sure that it was still there. It was.

He stood watching the Roller for a while. It was keeping a safe distance back from the barrier, out of effective stone-throwing range. It was moving around back there, doing something. He couldn't tell what it was doing.

Once it stopped moving, came a little closer, and seemed to concentrate its attention on him. Again Carson had to fight off a wave of nausea. He threw a stone at it and the Roller retreated and went back to whatever it had been doing before.

At least he could make it keep its distance.

And, he thought bitterly, a devil of a lot of good *that* did him. Just the same, he spent the next hour or two gathering stones of suitable size for throwing, and making several neat piles of them, near his side of the barrier.

His throat burned now. It was difficult for him to think about anything except water.

But he *had* to think about other things. About getting though that barrier, under or over it, getting at that red sphere and killing it before this place of heat and thirst killed him first.

The barrier went to the wall upon either side, but how high and how far under the sand?

For just a moment, Carson's mind was too fuzzy to think out how he could find out either of those things. Idly, sitting there in the hot sand—and he didn't remember sitting down—he watched a blue lizard crawl from the shelter of one bush to the shelter of another.

From under the second bush, it looked out at him.

Carson grinned at it. Maybe he was getting a bit punch-drunk, because he remembered suddenly the old story of the desert-colonists on Mars, taken from an older desert story of Earth—"Pretty soon you get so lonesome you find yourself talking to the lizards, and then not so long after that you find the lizards talking back to you—"

He should have been concentrating, of course, on how to kill the Roller, but instead he grinned at the lizard and said, "Hello, there."

The lizard took a few steps toward him. "Hello," it said.

Carson was stunned for a moment, and then he put back his head and roared with laughter. It didn't hurt his throat to do so, either; he hadn't been *that* thirsty.

Why not? Why should the Entity who thought up this nightmare of a place not have a sense of humor, along with the other powers he had? Talking lizards, equipped to talk back in my own language, if I talk to them— It's a nice touch.

He grinned at the lizard and said, "Come on over." But the lizard turned and ran away, scurrying from bush to bush until it was out of sight.

He was thirsty again.

And he had to *do* something. He couldn't win this contest by sitting here sweating and feeling miserable. He had to *do* something. But what?

Get through the barrier. But he couldn't get through it, or over it. But was he certain he couldn't get under it? And come to think of it, didn't one sometimes find water by digging? Two birds with one stone—

Painfully now, Carson limped up to the barrier and started digging, scooping up sand a double handful at a time. It was slow, hard work because the sand ran in at the edges and the deeper he got the bigger in diameter the hole had to be. How many hours it took him, he didn't know, but he hit bedrock four feet down. Dry bedrock; no sign of water.

And the force-field of the barrier went down clear to the bedrock. No dice. No water. Nothing.

He crawled out of the hole and lay there panting, and then raised his head to look across and see what the Roller was doing. It must be doing something back there.

It was. It was making something out of wood from the bushes, tied together with tendrils. A queerly shaped framework about four feet high and roughly square. To see it better, Carson climbed up onto the mound of sand he had excavated from the hole, and stood there staring.

There were two long levers sticking out of the back of it, one with a cup-shaped affair on the end of it. Seemed to be some sort of a catapult, Carson thought.

Sure enough, the Roller was lifting a sizable rock into the cup-shaped outfit. One of its tentacles moved the other lever up and down for awhile, and then it turned the machine slightly as though aiming it and the lever with the stone flew up and forward.

The stone raced several yards over Carson's head, so far away that he didn't have to duck, but he judged the distance it had traveled, and whistled softly. He couldn't throw a rock that weight more than half that distance. And even retreating to the rear of his domain wouldn't put him out of range of that machine, if the Roller shoved it forward almost to the barrier.

Another rock whizzed over. Not quite so far away this time.

That thing could be dangerous, he decided. Maybe he'd better do something about it.

Moving from side to side along the barrier, so the catapult couldn't bracket him, he whaled a dozen rocks at it. But that wasn't going to be any good, he saw. They had to be light rocks, or he couldn't throw them that far. If they hit the framework, they bounced off harmlessly. And the Roller had no difficulty, at that distance, in moving aside from those that came near it.

Besides, his arm was tiring badly. He ached all over from sheer weariness. If he could only rest awhile without having to duck rocks from that catapult at regular intervals of maybe thirty seconds each—

He stumbled back to the rear of the arena. Then he saw even that wasn't any good. The rocks reached back there, too, only there were longer intervals between them, as though it took longer to wind up the mechanism, whatever it was, of the catapult.

Wearily he dragged himself back to the barrier again. Several times he fell and could barely rise to his feet to go on. He was, he knew, near the limit of his endurance. Yet he didn't dare stop moving now, until and unless he could put that catapult out of action. If he fell asleep, he'd never wake up.

One of the stones from it gave him the first glimmer of an idea. It struck upon one of the piles of stones he'd gathered together near the barrier to use as ammunition, and it struck sparks.

Sparks. Fire. Primitive man had made fire by striking sparks, and with some of those dry crumbly bushes as tinder—

Luckily, a bush of that type was near him. He broke it off, took it over to a pile of stones, then patiently hit one stone against another until a spark touched the punklike wood of the bush. It went up in flames so fast that it singed his eyebrows and was burned to an ash within seconds.

But he had the idea now, and within minutes he had a little fire going in the lee of the mound of sand he'd made digging the hole an hour or two ago. Tinder bushes had started it, and other bushes which burned, but more slowly, kept it a steady flame.

The tough wirelike tendrils didn't burn readily; that made the fire-bombs easy to make and throw. A bundle of faggots tied about a small stone to give it weight and a loop of the tendril to swing it by.

He made half a dozen of them before he lighted and threw the first. It went wide, and the Roller started a quick retreat, pulling the catapult after it. But Carson had others ready and threw them in rapid succession. The fourth wedged in the catapult's framework, and did the trick. The Roller tried desperately to put out the spreading blaze by throwing sand, but its clawed tentacles would take only a spoonful at a time and its efforts were ineffectual. The catapult burned.

The Roller moved safely away from the fire and seemed to concentrate its attention on Carson and again he felt that wave of hatred and nausea. But more weakly; either the Roller itself was weakening or Carson had learned how to protect himself against the mental attack.

He thumbed his nose at it and then sent it scuttling back to safety by throwing a stone. The Roller went clear to the back of its half of the arena and started pulling up bushes again. Probably it was going to make another catapult.

Carson verified—for the hundredth time—that the barrier was still operating, and then found himself sitting in the sand beside it because he was suddenly too weak to stand up.

His leg throbbed steadily now and the pangs of thirst were severe. But those things paled beside the utter physical exhaustion that gripped his entire body.

And the heat.

Hell must be like this, he thought. The hell that the ancients had believed in. He fought to stay awake, and yet staying awake seemed futile, for there was nothing he could do. Nothing, while the barrier remained impregnable and the Roller stayed back out of range.

But there must be *something*. He tried to remember things he had read in books of archaeology about the methods of fighting used back in the days before metal and plastic. The stone missile, that had come first, he thought. Well, that he already had.

The only improvement on it would be a catapult, such as the Roller had made. But he'd never be able to make one, with the tiny bits of wood available from the bushes— no single piece longer than a foot or so. Certainly he could figure out a mechanism for one, but he didn't have the endurance left for a task that would take days.

Days? But the Roller had made one. Had they been here days already? Then he remembered that the Roller had many tentacles to work with and undoubtedly could do such work faster than he.

And besides, a catapult wouldn't decide the issue. He had to do better than that.

Bow and arrow? No; he had tried archery once and knew his own ineptness with a bow. Even with a modern sportsman's durasteel weapon, made for accuracy. With such a crude, pieced-together outfit as he could make here, he doubted if he could shoot as far as he could throw a rock, and knew he couldn't shoot as straight.

Spear? Well, he *could* make that. It would be useless as a throwing weapon at any distance, but would be a handy thing at close range, if he ever got to close range.

And making one would give him something to do. Help keep his mind from wandering, as it was beginning to do. Sometimes now, he had to concentrate awhile before he could remember why he was here, why he had to kill the Roller.

Luckily he was still beside one of the piles of stones. He sorted through it until he found one shaped roughly like a spearhead. With a smaller stone he began to chip it into shape, fashioning sharp shoulders on the sides so that if it penetrated it would not pull out again.

Like a harpoon? There was something in that idea, he thought. A harpoon was better than a spear, maybe, for this crazy contest. If he could once get it into the Roller, and have a rope on it, he could pull the Roller up against the barrier and the stone blade of his knife would reach through that barrier, even if his hands wouldn't.

The shaft was harder to make than the head. But by splitting and joining the main stems of four of the bushes, and wrapping the joints with the tough but thin tendrils, he got a strong shaft about four feet long, and tied the stone head in a notch cut in the end.

It was crude, but strong.

And the rope. With the thin tough tendrils he made himself twenty feet of line. It was light and didn't look strong, but he knew it would hold his weight and to spare. He tied one end of it to the shaft of the harpoon and the other end about his right wrist. At least, if he threw his harpoon across the barrier, he'd be able to pull it back if he missed.

Then when he had tied the last knot and there was nothing more he could do, the heat and the weariness and the pain in his leg and the dreadful thirst were suddenly a thousand times worse than they had been before.

He tried to stand up, to see what the Roller was doing now, and found he couldn't get to his feet. On the third try, he got as far as his knees and then fell flat again.

"I've got to sleep," he thought. "If a showdown came now, I'd be helpless. He could come up here and kill me, if he knew. I've got to regain some strength."

Slowly, painfully, he crawled back away from the barrier. Ten yards, twenty—

The jar of something thudding against the sand near him waked him from a confused and horrible dream to a more confused and more horrible reality, and he opened his eyes again to the blue radiance over blue sand.

How long had he slept? A minute? A day?

Another stone thudded nearer and threw sand on him. He got his arms under him and sat up. He turned around and saw the Roller twenty yards away, at the barrier.

It rolled away hastily as he sat up, not stopping until it was as far away as it could get.

He'd fallen asleep too soon, he realized, while he was still in range of the Roller's throwing ability. Seeing him lying motionless, it had dared to come up to the barrier and throw stones at him. Luckily, it didn't realize how weak he was, or it could have stayed there and kept on throwing stones.

Had he slept long? He didn't think so, because he felt just as he had before. Not rested at all, no thirstier, no different. Probably he'd been there only a few minutes.

He started crawling again, this time forcing himself to keep going until he was as far as he could go, until the colorless, opaque wall of the arena's outer shell was only a yard away.

Then things slipped away again—

When he awoke, nothing about him was changed, but this time he knew that he had slept a long time.

The first thing he became aware of was the inside of his mouth; it was dry, caked. His tongue was swollen.

Something was wrong, he knew, as he returned slowly to full awareness. He felt less tired, the stage of utter exhaustion had passed. The sleep had taken care of that.

But there was pain, agonizing pain. It wasn't until he tried to move that he knew that it came from his leg.

He raised his head and looked down at it. It was swollen terribly below the knee and the swelling showed even halfway up his thigh. The plant tendrils he had used to tie on the protective pad of leaves now cut deeply into the swollen flesh.

To get his knife under that imbedded lashing would have been impossible. Fortunately, the final knot was over the shin bone, in front, where the vine cut in less deeply than elsewhere. He was able, after an agonizing effort, to untie the knot.

A look under the pad of leaves told him the worst. Infection and blood poisoning, both pretty bad and getting worse.

And without drugs, without cloth, without even *water,* there wasn't even a thing he could do about it.

Not a thing, except *die,* when the poison had spread through his system.

He knew it was hopeless, then, and that he'd lost.

And with him, humanity. When he died here, out there in the universe he knew, all his friends, everybody, would die too. And Earth and the colonized planets would be the home of the red, rolling alien Outsiders. Creatures out of a nightmare, things without a human attribute, who picked lizards apart for the fun of it.

It was the thought of that which gave him courage to start crawling, almost blindly in pain, toward the barrier again. Not crawling on his hands and knees this time, but pulling himself along only by his arms and hands.

A chance in a million, that maybe he'd have the strength left, when he got there, to throw his harpoon-spear just *once,* and with deadly effect, if—on another chance in a million—the Roller would come up to the barrier. Or if the barrier was gone, now.

It took him years, it seemed, to get there.

The barrier wasn't gone. It was as impassable as when he'd first felt it.

And the Roller wasn't at the barrier. By raising up on his elbows, he could see it at the back of its part of the arena, working on a wooden framework that was a half-completed duplicate of the catapult he'd destroyed.

It was moving slowly now. Undoubtedly it had weakened, too.

But Carson doubted that it would ever need that second catapult. He'd be dead, he thought, before it was finished.

If he could attract it to the barrier, now, while he was still alive— He waved an arm and tried to shout, but his parched throat would make no sound.

Or if he could get through the barrier—

His mind must have slipped for a moment, for he found himself beating his fists against the barrier in futile rage, and made himself stop.

He closed his eyes, tried to make himself calm.

"Hello," said the voice.

It was a small, thin voice. It sounded like—

He opened his eyes and turned his head. It *was* the lizard.

"Go away," Carson wanted to say. "Go away, you're not really there, or you're there but not really talking. I'm imagining things again."

But he couldn't talk; his throat and tongue were past all speech with the dryness. He closed his eyes again.

"Hurt," said the voice. "Kill. Hurt—kill. Come."

He opened his eyes again. The blue ten-legged lizard was still there. It ran a little way along the barrier, came back, started off again, and came back.

"Hurt," it said. "Kill. Come."

Again it started off, and came back. Obviously it wanted Carson to follow it along the barrier.

He closed his eyes again. The voice kept on. The same three meaningless words. Each time he opened his eyes, it ran off and came back.

"Hurt. Kill. Come."

Carson groaned. There would be no peace unless he followed the blasted thing. Like it wanted him to.

He followed it, crawling. Another sound, a high-pitched squealing. Something small, blue, that looked like a lizard and yet didn't—

Then he saw what it was—the lizard whose legs the Roller had pulled off, so long ago. But it wasn't dead; it had come back to life and was wriggling and screaming in agony.

"Hurt," said the other lizard. "Hurt. Kill. Kill."

Carson understood. He took the flint knife from his belt and killed the tortured creature. The live lizard scurried off quickly.

Carson turned back to the barrier. He leaned his hands and head against it and watched the Roller, far back, working on the new catapult.

"I couldn't get that far," he thought, "if I could get through. If I could get through, I might win yet. It looks weak, too. I might—"

And then there was another reaction of black hopelessness, when pain snapped his will and he wished that he were dead. He envied the lizard he'd just killed. It didn't have to live on and suffer. And he did. It would be hours, it might be days, before the blood poisoning killed him.

If only he could use that knife on himself—

But he knew he wouldn't. As long as he was alive, there was the millionth chance—

He was straining, pushing on the barrier with the flat of his hands, and he noticed his arms, how thin and scrawny they were now. He must really have been here a long time, for days, to get as thin as that.

How much longer now, before he died? How much more heat and thirst and pain could flesh stand?

For a little while he was almost hysterical again, and then came a time of deep calm, and a thought that was startling.

The lizard he had just killed. *It had crossed the barrier, still alive.* It had come from the Roller's side; the Roller had pulled off its legs and then tossed it contemptuously at him and it had come through the barrier. He'd thought, because the lizard was dead.

But it hadn't been dead; it had been unconscious.

A live lizard couldn't go through the barrier, but an unconscious one could. The barrier was not barrier, then, to living flesh, but to conscious flesh. It was a *mental* projection, a *mental* hazard.

And with that thought, Carson started crawling along the barrier to make his last desperate gamble. A hope so forlorn that only a dying man would have dared try it.

No use weighing the odds of success. Not when, if he didn't try it, those odds were infinitely to zero.

He crawled along the barrier to the dune of sand, about four feet high, which he'd scooped out in trying—how many days ago?—to dig under the barrier or to reach water.

That mound was right at the barrier, its farther slope half on one side of the barrier, half on the other.

Taking with him a rock from the pile nearby, he climbed up to the top of the dune and over the top, and lay there against the barrier, his weight leaning against it so that if the barrier were taken away he'd roll on down the short slope into the enemy territory.

He checked to be sure that the knife was safely in his rope belt, that the harpoon was in the crook of his left arm and that the twenty-foot rope was fastened to it and to his wrist.

Then with his right hand he raised the rock with which he would hit himself on the head. Luck would have to be with him on that blow; it would have to be hard enough to knock him out, but not hard enough to knock him out for long.

He had a hunch that the Roller was watching him, and would see him roll down through the barrier, and come to investigate. It would think he was dead, he hoped—he thought it had probably drawn the same deduction about the nature of the barrier that he had drawn. But it would come cautiously. He would have a little time—

He struck.

Pain brought him back to consciousness. A sudden, sharp pain in his hip that was differing from the throbbing pain in his head and the throbbing pain in his leg.

But he had, thinking things out before he had struck himself, anticipated that very pain, even hoped for it, and had steeled himself against awakening with a sudden movement.

He lay still, but opened his eyes just a slit, and saw that he had guessed rightly. The Roller was coming closer. It was twenty feet away and the pain that had awakened him was the stone it had tossed to see whether he was alive or dead.

He lay still. It came closer, fifteen feet away, and stopped again. Carson scarcely breathed.

As nearly as possible, he was keeping his mind a blank, lest its telepathic ability detect consciousness in him. And with his mind blanked out that way, the impact of its thoughts upon his mind was nearly soul-shattering.

He felt sheer horror at the utter *alienness,* the *differentness* of those thoughts. Things that he felt but could not understand and could never express, because no terrestrial language had words, no terrestrial mind had images to fit them. The mind of a spider, he thought, or the mind of a praying mantis or a Martian sand-serpent, raised to intelligence and put in telepathic rapport with human minds, would be a homely familiar thing, compared to this.

He understood now the Entity had been right: Man or Roller, and the universe was not a place that could hold them both. Farther apart than god and devil, there could never be even a balance between them.

Closer. Carson waited until it was only four feet away, until its clawed tentacles reached out—

Oblivious to agony now, he sat up, raised and flung the harpoon with all the strength that remained in him. Or he thought it was all; sudden final strength flooded through him, along with a sudden forgetfulness of pain as definite as a nerve block.

As the Roller, deeply stabbed by the harpoon, rolled away, Carson tried to get to his feet to run after it. He couldn't do that; he fell, but kept crawling.

It reached the end of the rope, and he was jerked forward by the pull of his wrist. It dragged him a few feet and then stopped. Carson kept on going, pulling himself toward it hand over hand along the rope.

It stopped there, writhing tentacles trying in vain to pull out the harpoon. It seemed to shudder and quiver, and then it must have realized that it couldn't get away, for it rolled back toward him, clawed tentacles reaching out.

Stone knife in hand, he met it. He stabbed, again and again, while those horrid claws ripped skin and flesh and muscle from his body.

He stabbed and slashed, and at last it was still.

A bell was ringing, and it took a while after he'd opened his eyes to tell where he was and what it was. He was strapped into the seat of his scouter, and the visiplate before him showed only empty space. No Outsider ship and no impossible planet.

The bell was the communications plate signal; someone wanted him to switch power into the receiver. Purely reflex action enabled him to reach forward and throw the lever.

The face of Brander, captain of the *Magellan*, mother-ship of his group of scouters, flashed into the screen. His face was pale and his black eyes glowed with excitement.

"*Magellan* to Carson," he snapped. "Come on in. The fight's over. We've won!"

The screen went blank; Brander would be signaling the other scouters of his command.

Slowly, Carson set the controls for the return. Slowly, unbelievingly, he unstrapped himself from the seat and went back to get a drink at the cold-water tank. For some reason, he was unbelievably thirsty. He drank six glasses.

He leaned there against the wall, trying to think.

Had it happened? He was in good health, sound, uninjured. His thirst had been mental rather than physical; his throat hadn't been dry. His leg—

He pulled up his trouser leg and looked at the calf. There was a long white scar there, but a perfectly healed scar. It hadn't been there before. He zipped open the front of his shirt and saw that his chest and abdomen were criss-crossed with tiny, almost unnoticeable perfectly healed scars.

It *had* happened.

The scouter, under automatic control, was already entering the hatch of the mother-ship. The grapples pulled it into its individual lock, and a moment later a buzzer indicated that the lock was air-filled. Carson opened the hatch and stepped outside, went through the double door of the lock.

He went right to Brander's office, went in, and saluted.

Brander still looked dizzily dazed. "Hi, Carson," he said. "What you missed! What a show!"

"What happened, sir?"

"Don't know exactly. We fired one salvo, and their whole fleet went up in dust! Whatever it was jumped from ship to ship in a flash, even the ones we hadn't aimed at and that were out of range! The whole fleet disintegrated before our eyes, and we didn't get the paint of a single ship scratched!

"We can't even claim credit for it. Must have been some unstable component in the metal they used, and our sighting shot just set it off. Man, oh man, too bad you missed all the excitement."

Carson managed to grin. It was a sickly ghost of a grin, for it would be days before he'd be over the mental impact of his experience, but the captain wasn't watching, and didn't notice.

"Yes, sir," he said. Common sense, more than modesty, told him he'd be branded forever as the worst liar in space if he ever said any more than that. "Yes, sir, too bad I missed all the excitement."

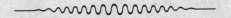

FREDRIC BROWN *was one of the great science fiction writers of the 1940s and 1950s, especially known for his short stories and short-short stories; although he also wrote a few science fiction novels (including* Martians, Go Home!*) and a host of mystery novels, many of them featuring the amateur detective team of uncle and nephew, Ambrose and Ed Hunter. "Arena" is his best-known and most successful story, having inspired both a* Star Trek *and an* Outer Limits *episode.*

Sooner or later, all young people have to make a choice between the way their parents want them to live and the way their peers want them to live. But for Aggie, "The Choice" is a lot bigger than for most girls— and she has to make it very fast indeed, and under a lot of pressure.

The Choice

Adaptation by Diane Duane
Original screenplay by Anne Lewis Hamilton

SCHOOL PLAYGROUNDS acquire a terrible sameness over the years: especially when you're in them, again and again, and no one will speak to you. This was just one more, like many others; the usual games of hopscotch and Chinese jump rope going on, the usual deadly arguments taking place over whether the "potsy" had come down on the chalk line, complaints that someone was using the wrong chant—too fast or slow for the specific jump rope variant being used. A murderous game of kickball was in progress off to one side, among a crowd of boys deep in the throes of early male bonding.

No one saw, or at least no one would willingly have admitted to seeing, the fourth grader standing by herself next to the potted pine tree . . . carefully watching, without appearing to watch, all the activity going on around her. Aggie had learned a long time ago not to make it at all obvious that you were watching. That only made it worse when they realized you were doing it. And it made it worse for you inside when, after one more day, it became plain that none of them would ever notice you as anything except as a nuisance, an object of scorn: the last one picked in every game . . . or, rather, never picked, but forced on one team or another as the "leftover," the useless one.

Aggie wasn't ugly. She wasn't too fat for her age, or too thin, or too tall or too short; her long blonde hair wasn't unfashionable. There was nothing weird about her clothes or her shoes; they weren't old, they weren't out of style. She didn't have a harelip or a club foot. Nonetheless, she was different. She knew it. *They* knew it. But she was not going to give them the satisfaction of letting them know that she had, long ago, hopelessly accepted their evaluation.

The soccer game got a little out of control; the ball rolled over toward her. Aggie stopped it with one foot, more or less unconsciously, and looked at it as if it was an alien life-form. She didn't hear the voice speaking to her for a moment.

"Oh, not again! Kick it back, scum-wad."

Her eyes flicked up to the speaker—a grim look from under her brows. It was Clark: small for his age, pugnacious, fast-mouthed, and sometimes cowardly when you least expected it. He was one of the ones she could have said she hated, if the word didn't imply more energy than Aggie normally expended on him.

"Did you hear me?" Clark said, clearly unbelieving that this waste of time should be making him waste his time further.

"I'm not a scum-wad," Aggie said.

Clark ambled forward with a look of amused pleasure on his face. Aggie could almost see what he was thinking, as if it were printed in blurry ink on blotting paper. He would look good in front of the others, and get some fun out of this as well. "Okay," Clark said, the grin beginning to spread, "you're not a scum-wad. You're a scum-*pile*."

Aggie merely looked at him for a moment. The others readily took up the cry, "Aggie is a scum-pile . . . Aggie is a scum-pile. . . ."

Aggie's eyes narrowed. "Get away from me," she said.

He moved a couple of steps closer. "Make us," Clark said, smiling broadly now, confident in Aggie's helplessness. What could she do about eleven of them, all jeering at her at once, except make a scene—run to a teacher, claiming that she was being bullied? And then they would have a new word to shout at her, tomorrow, or today on the way home from school: "crybaby, crybaby!" It would go on for days. "Can't take a joke . . . can't handle it. . . ."

Aggie had heard it all before. Sometimes she had tried not to react, feeling in a vague way that there was something wrong with that approach. But the feeling hadn't lasted. Lately, she had been giving in to the urge more than usual. Lately, she had discovered how good it could feel. *You asked for it,* she thought.

The crowd of kids pointed and jeered, and moved closer. The movement decided her. Aggie looked at Clark, but more importantly, she looked at the field of pallid light around him, like heat haze over a pavement—hardly there, but there enough for her to see, to use. Aggie picked a spot where the pale currents flowed together, and thought, *Something. Anything. Just make him stop . . . make them stop . . . make it—*

Abruptly, Clark yelled, and leaned forward holding his nose. As if someone had rewritten the headline on the blotting paper of his mind, it became obvious that all the joy was gone from his moment. Suddenly Clark was bleeding; something had hit him. Something had—

Clark looked at Aggie, shocked, and more than that, frightened. She waited for the riposte; there had to be one—that was the law of the playground. Clark wiped the blood away, and muttered to Aggie the words she had wanted to shout, or cry, enough times: "I'm gonna tell!" The other kids, their ringleader suddenly gone silent, were already beginning to wander away; now Clark turned and headed off after them, growing furious as well as frightened. Now he was going to have to explain what happened, somehow . . . and he couldn't.

Neither could Aggie, exactly. But as she watched him go, she smiled a little, thinly.

There would be trouble, now. There was almost always trouble, these days. But sometimes it was worth it.

Later, though, sitting on the bench out in the cold hallway—why was it that no matter how many radiators they put in a school hallway, it was always cold?—and overhearing the usual complaints and explanations from inside the principal's office, Aggie sat considering her hands, folded in her lap, and wondered, *is it really worth it? Is there ever going to be a time when this doesn't happen?* Or would the rest of her life be like this—forever being hauled up in front of people who have power over you, mostly power that they use to get you in trouble, and the trouble always getting worse. . . .

The voices carried surprisingly well from inside the office. *You'd think,* Aggie thought, *if they wanted to keep anything private in there, they'd do something about the soundproofing.* But maybe it had been too long since the people who should have taken care of that had been kids themselves, so that they could no longer remember how sharp your ears were, especially when you were listening hard for every word that came through that door.

"This is the fifth incident in as many weeks," said the principal's voice. "One girl claims she was pushed off the top of the slide. We had a classroom that looked like the Tasmanian Devil went through it." Aggie rolled her eyes at that one; it hadn't been nearly that bad, but no one was going to be willing to admit as much after the fact. *Why am I even bothering to listen to this?* Aggie thought. *Why should I care? No one's going to cut me any slack. Things are just going to get worse.*

I wish I was dead. . . .

Inside the office, the principal, a handsome gray-haired woman in her late forties, was saying a little helplessly, "As always, Aggie says she had nothing to do with it."

Joe and Leslie Travis looked at each other. "We know Aggie's had some emotional problems, and we're looking for a new therapist. But the others pick on her. . . ." said Leslie, sadly. Joe said, "She'll get better . . . if you could just give her one more chance. . . ."

The principal sighed. Sitting in front of her, as they had done a number of times before, were a nice young professional couple, well-adjusted as far as she could tell, not abusive as far as she could tell—though these days you found yourself looking twice at everyone for signs that might betray something of the kind. The first couple of times they had sat here, they had mostly just looked impatient. They couldn't take seriously the idea that their daughter was any kind of problem. Now, though, they were starting to look scared. They had reason, and the principal very much wished they didn't, but there was nothing she could do about it.

"Mr. Travis," she said, "the problem is the other parents. They claim that we're putting their children in an unsafe environment, and that we're legally liable." She saw the incredulous look on their faces and felt the regret more strongly still. "I'm sorry, but I must insist Aggie be removed from this school. . . ."

Aggie's mother sat briefly with her mouth open in astonishment, and then said, "Where are we supposed to put her? A reform school? She's ten years old."

The principal looked at her with some compunction. "You might try a school for children with special needs."

Leslie stared, and looked offended. "'Special needs'? My daughter is not retarded."

Sadly, the principal said, "No one is saying that. In fact, if it weren't for her behavioral problems, this meeting would be about moving Aggie forward a grade. . . ." She looked a little unhappily at her folded hands. "But her behavior is disruptive, uncontrollable, and. . . ." There she paused.

"'And' what?"

She had to say it. "Dangerous."

Joe stared at the principal, incredulousness beginning to turn to anger. "That's ridiculous. I know Aggie has problems . . . maybe makes a mess every now and then . . . but she says she didn't hurt anyone. . . ."

The principal pursed her lips and said, "Clark Howell didn't hit himself in the nose."

The parents looked at each other uneasily. They had come in wearing the 'reasonable' expression that the principal knew well, a look that said 'let's talk it through.' It was doing them no good, though; they knew it, and the facade was starting to crack. Aggie's father said, "Maybe one of the other kids. . . ."

The principal felt bad for them, but there was no point in letting this go on any further. "I'm sorry," she said. "I'm going to have to suspend Aggie from the next two weeks of school—the rest of the term." She stood up.

So did Aggie's mother, her face twisting with disbelief and anger. "This is ridiculous! You can't do this to my child!" She turned and made her way toward the door a little unsteadily, like someone suddenly having trouble seeing through full eyes.

Aggie's father stood, watching his wife go, then turned back toward the principal. "The other parents," he said, "aren't the only ones who can file suit, you know." And he went out after Aggie's mother.

The principal stood and watched him go, then sat down slowly, and folded her hands again, feeling as helpless as they.

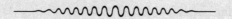

It was a nice home, out in one of the most pleasant suburbs of town; plenty of room, an old converted Victorian—the American dream home, except that the dream had become somewhat corrupted of late. Leslie, in her bathrobe, walked into the bedroom and shut the door quietly. She hung up the bathrobe and went to sit by her husband on the bed.

"Has she gone to bed?"

"Almost." She hugged Joe one-armed, shaking her head, and leaned against him wearily. "It's so hard, Joe. She won't *talk* to me."

"It's the same with me."

Joe stared at the bedspread as if it held the answer to the problem. "She can't understand why we won't believe her. I think she really feels betrayed. What are we going to do with her?"

Leslie breathed in, breathed out, and shook her own head. Very faintly she could remember the sinking feeling that came with those times in her childhood when *she* had been in trouble, and no one had understood, or could be made to understand, what the problem had been. Now she could no longer even remember what those troubles had been, but at the time, they had seemed to fill the whole world. Her heart ached for her daughter, who now seemed to be going through something similar . . . and was no better at telling her what the trouble was than she had been at getting through to her own parents. *I swore it wasn't going to be like this,* she thought, *but I seem to be failing. . . .*

"I don't know, honey," Joe said at last. "I think we should get someone for Aggie."

Leslie looked at him in surprise. "What do you mean, 'get someone'?"

"A full-time live-in who can take some of the burden off us. Maybe there's someone who specializes in problem kids. Someone at work mentioned a new agency. . . ."

Leslie shook her head again, this time in denial. "Joe, we can't afford that—we're already stretched."

He sighed. "I can pull in some more hours. I've already spoken to Frank about it. Besides, right now, I really don't think we have a choice."

Leslie sat still for a couple of moments, rapidly doing household mathematics in her head. Their finances were balanced precariously enough as it was; the thought of the added expense of a live-in nanny, especially one with enough training to make any kind of difference to Aggie, gave her serious pause. "But what if this doesn't work either?" she said. "I mean, even if we found somebody, how long do you think we could keep them—with a little girl who hurts other kids, who lies all the time?"

Her husband looked at her uncertainly. "We don't *know* she lies. . . ."

Leslie looked at her husband with slight exasperation. "Oh, come on, Joe! Things break—Aggie says she didn't do it. Someone gets hit in the face—she didn't do it. The fish tank breaks—she didn't do it."

"Look—" Joe turned away, looking unhappy. "I don't want to get into this right now. We'll burn that bridge when we come to it. Meanwhile, we've got other things to think about. Checking that local agency—maybe even putting ads in the paper."

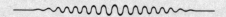

In the big comfortable bathroom, Aggie sat on the clothes hamper next to the toilet, head bent a little to one side, listening. Here, too, the grownups had no idea of how sound traveled—Aggie wondered whether it had something to do with the hot-air registers going through the bedroom before they came to the bathroom. Though, it was true, there were lots of other places where she seemed to be able to hear what was going on without hot-air registers being involved. She was holding her old clown doll, one that she had affectionate feelings for even this far along in her childhood, even though she knew she should ditch such things before the kids at school found out about them and made her situation even worse. Though at the moment it seemed like school was not going to be a problem: the trouble was going to relocate itself to home.

Aggie let out a long, troubled breath, and hugged the clown. Once, she remembered, holding that doll could make her feel that everything was going to turn out right, even when cold reason said otherwise. *Not any more.*

The voices went on outside, discussing her as if she was some kind of abstract problem. Problem: *that* was what she was now—what she had become. Not a person, but something broken, like a malfunctioning appliance; something that simply needed fixing so that life would go back to its normal smooth course.

"—someone who could take some of the pressure off us—"

Aggie stood up silently at the sound of that, leaning closer to the wall, where she could hear better. *Oh, wonderful,* she thought. A *zookeeper . . . someone with a whip and a chair.* And it was going to happen, too—she knew that tone of voice from her father. There was nothing she could do to stop it.

"—specializes in problem kids—" Aggie grimaced. Problem! *And you've always been one,* said a nasty voice in the back of her mind. *Ever since you found out that you could.*

She turned away, trying to stifle the thought, but it wouldn't be stifled. They were going to get someone who would live here, spy on her, protect them from her—like some kind of cop. The anger began to well up inside Aggie. In the bedroom—but also, somehow, inside her—she could hear the argument going on, the accusations being passed back and forth, all the more painful for being made in such a matter-of-fact tone. Couldn't they see it? Couldn't they see how wrong they were? But they couldn't. . . .

Aggie looked at herself in the mirror, wondering, was this the face of the kid who did the kind of things they were talking about? She let the anger rise, making an angry buzzing sound in the air. For the moment, she liked the way it felt. She didn't care.

The bell-shaped light fixture that jutted from the wall beside the mirror flickered: the bulb jingled, as if something was wrong with the filament. The light fixture began to tremble a little. The mirror shook. The shaking got worse. *Go on,* Aggie thought. *Go on, I don't care. Let it happen. Let it—*

And, obediently, it began. Cupboards flew open. Bottles and jars leapt out to smash angrily on the floor. The faucets on the sink and the tub all turned, and water spat out of them with furious force. The hamper on which Aggie had been sitting flipped its lid open and ejected all the dirty laundry up into the air and onto the floor. The toilet flushed, and flushed again. Mouthwash bottles and shaving cream cans began spraying their contents all over the place. Even the toothpaste squirted itself into the sink.

From outside the sound of the argument suddenly stopping. That, at least, was good. But then came the sound of the pounding on the door. "What the hell is that?"

"Aggie! Let us in!"

"Open the door!"

Suddenly it was all too much; the noise, the fierce buzz in the air, like a swarm of bees clotting together in rage, thickening everything with the dark stinging smell of anger. Aggie began to feel as if she was not the source of it, but the target; as if it would turn in on her, attack her next. She covered her ears, squeezed her eyes shut, and squealed with fright.

The pounding got louder. Then, all in a rush, her parents got in. Aggie stood there, suddenly deathly tired, feeling the sudden wash of forces around her ebb away, the buzzing go quiet. It was over. Her mother and father stood there and looked in shock at the incredible mess.

"Oh, God . . ." her mother said, astonished.

Her father turned on her, furious. "Aggie—what's going on?"

She didn't know how to begin telling him: the right words simply did not exist. How did you describe the fury that came whining out of you, looking for somewhere to come to roost—and then turned on you, too? How did you even begin describing the helpless feeling as it rose in you again—no way to stop it, no way—and the angry tang of satisfaction as the outer world, however briefly, reflected the turmoil of the inner? But then there was the fear, afterwards—always the fear. And it was no better now that she saw that face, usually so loving, going dark with anger. Aggie started to tremble. "Everything just started shaking—"

"By *itself*?" Her father was in no mood for strange explanations, if he ever had been. Hope died in Aggie one more time. "Look at this mess! Damnit, this is gonna stop! Do you hear me?"

Her mother moved close to her, reached out to hold her. "Joe! You're frightening her! She's only a child!"

He opened his mouth to reply, fierce, but didn't get a chance. Aggie cried, "I don't know *why* this happened!

Why don't you believe me?" She threw him one last angry glance—*why aren't you able to fix this? Why aren't you able to help?*—and fled down to her bedroom.

"Damnit, Joe," she heard her mother say bitterly.

Her husband passed a hand over his face. "I'm sorry. I never did that before—"

Leslie went after Aggie. The crash of broken glass preceded her. "Oh, damnit. Aggie—"

Unsmellable except to one person there, the scent of despair filled the Travis house.

The outside of the shop was a handsome turn-of-the-century arched red-brick facade, with a sign in the window that said 'Antiquarius Books.' Inside, the place had little of the shiny organization common to the big chain bookshops. Buried in among the shelves was a desk covered with the usual clutter of a successful bookshop: order forms, notes and more notes, books new and old stacked up high. The shelves were neatly enough arranged, but more books were stacked and piled up on top of them.

The phone rang. The bookstore's owner picked it up. "Antiquarius Books . . ."

The phone squeaked softly in her ear for a moment. The owner looked up and back to the second desk, buried even further back toward the rear of the store. "Jean," the owner said, "have we got any paperback copies of that new Margaret Atwood novel?"

Sitting behind the rear desk was another woman; gray-haired, possibly in her fifties, handsome enough, but with a face seamed with wary lines, the kind of face that suggested its owner had had her lack of faith in human nature justified entirely too many times. Her desk was covered with newspapers, some slightly ragged for having had clippings cut out of them. Even as the woman spoke, she was turning over pages of the topmost newspaper as if looking for something; and she answered almost offhandedly. "We'll have a couple in later this week."

"Check with us Friday, why don't you?" said her partner to the person on the other end of the phone. "You're welcome."

She hung up and leaned back a little, looking down toward the end of the store. "I don't know how you do it," she said.

Jean smiled very slightly. "Do what?"

"Keep all these things in your head at the same time you're reading all those newspapers and talking on the phone."

Jean shrugged, turning over another page of the newspaper, then stopped, looking down at one particular article. Beside it was a picture of a young girl, a pretty child with a high forehead and long blonde hair. "I guess I've always been able to . . . change gears."

"You should do one of those self-help tapes," her partner said.

"Maybe I will." Jean read down through the rest of the article, looked at it thoughtfully for a moment. Then she lifted the receiver of her own phone, dialed it, waited.

It made a soft sound in her ear, and she said, "Hello . . . it's Jean. I've got another prospect for you."

A moment's more squeaking. "I know you just came in," Jean said softly, "but Rachel and Sarah are busy with others. The location is Eugene, Oregon, and the family name is Travis. . . ."

The conversation went on for a little while more. Finally Jean put down the phone and turned her attention back to the newspaper she had been looking at, folding it carefully and putting it underneath her desk. *Oh, let this be what I think it is,* she thought. *Please. . . .*

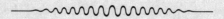

Outside the Travis home, on the front stoop, a group of well-dressed women were standing. Some of them were looking thoughtfully at the others with carefully applied smiles; some were refusing to look at the others at all.

Karen walked up slowly toward the steps, eyeing the other women as she came. All of them were plainly applicants for the same job. She smiled a little at them as she came up the steps. She already had a job. It was this one.

"Are you all here for the live-in job?" she said, cordially enough. "I thought I was early."

"I think we all had the same idea," said one of the other women, "getting here first, I mean. It's so tough to get these jobs these days, with all the competition. We all wanted to make the first impression."

Karen nodded. "I know what you mean."

"Not that I'm worried," said the woman who had spoken first; and she glanced at the others as she spoke, self-assured. "I'm probably the most qualified. I've got a degree in early childhood development from Brown."

Karen smiled at her a little bit, sat down on the porch railing. These women as a group looked like a small convention of Sunday school teachers: possibly that was exactly the impression they were trying to project. Karen was the most casually dressed of them: a big comfortable top, leggings, an overjacket, a Buster Brown hat. She had long blonde hair, and a wide mouth, and eyes that would not look away from the others': a young face, and in some strange way, a fearless one. "I like your dress," she said to the first woman.

"Thank you," the woman said.

Karen's gaze stayed steady a little longer than was normal. The other woman returned it, sensing a challenge of some kind. Then she began to frown, and put a hand to her head.

"Are you all right?" Karen said.

The woman held her head, glanced at Karen briefly. "I get these migraines," she said. "I'll be okay. . . ."

"Are you sure?" Karen said, not taking her gaze from the woman.

The woman blinked, took a breath, then another one. "Maybe not," she said, wincing. "Excuse me. . . ." She went down the steps slowly and carefully, holding on to the railing, and made her way down the street with great care.

Karen watched her go, then looked at the next woman, a pretty and nannyish looking woman in a pink sweater and dark skirt. She smiled at her in a friendly way. "I like your dress," she said softly. . . .

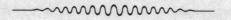

Only a few minutes later, Joe opened the front door and looked out. "We're ready to see the first—" he said, and then stopped, confused. There was only one woman.

"Hi," she said. "I'm Karen Ross."

"Oh. Okay." Joe looked around again, as if expecting the other women to reappear suddenly. He *had* seen them out the window; there had been at least six of them. . . . Bemused, he waved the young blonde woman through the door. She stepped past him, smiling charmingly; Joe paused to scan the porch one more time, then went in after her and shut the door behind them.

Inside, Joe and his wife looked over Karen's resumé. Karen stood calmly by a window, chatting with them in such a relaxed way that she might have been the one interviewing *them*.

"Karen Ross," she said to Leslie. "I'm from a large family. And I love kids."

"How big is your family?" Leslie asked.

"There were eight of us. I was the oldest, so I helped out a lot."

"Eight!" Joe said. He had trouble imagining what it must be like to deal with so many. One was turning out to be more than enough. . . .

"Now . . . you've just got the one child?" Karen said.

Joe's wife nodded. "Aggie. She's ten."

"Ten is a wonderful age."

"We have to tell you—" Aggie's mother stopped. From the corner of her eye, Joe knew that she could just see, peering through the stair rails, the small, pale face; Aggie, listening. He understood why she felt guilty about saying anything more. But she had to tell the truth, even so.

"There've been some problems," Joe said, trying to help her.

"What kind of problems?" Karen said.

Aggie's mother actually wrung her hands in embarrassment. "At first the doctors thought it was attention deficit disorder. But it could be worse than that."

The pale face behind the railing didn't change. Joe felt as if someone had put a knife into him, and was twisting it slowly. But if there was any way they were going to get help for their child, this was the way it was going to have to be . . . and Aggie would have to cope. "She just gets a little—there've been some problems at school," he said. "With other kids."

"And she sometimes breaks things," Leslie said.

"Breaks things?" said Karen.

"Her toys, sometimes dishes. Those kinds of things."

Joe looked up at Karen, a sad expression: the look of a man who hated to have to be saying this kind of thing. "But she's a very sweet girl."

Somewhat to his astonishment, Karen didn't look particularly concerned about the warning. "I'd like to meet her," Karen said.

Joe got up and headed up the hallway.

Leslie gestured at the nearby sofa: Karen sat down, again with that extraordinary self-assurance. *Of course,* Leslie thought, *it* is *a sellers' market for this kind of work. If she doesn't . . . if we don't. . . .* She chopped the thought off. "Your last job," she said to Karen, looking at the resumé again, "why did you leave?"

"The family moved to Hawaii. They wanted to take me with them, but I really didn't want to relocate so far from the mainland. You could call, their number's there." Karen smiled. "Two little boys . . . they were adorable."

Leslie played with the pages of the resumé again for a minute or so. After a few silent breaths, the sound of footsteps came from down the hall. The wearer of the small, pale face walked into the room, or maybe trudged was a better word. Leslie looked at her with feelings of both desperation and an odd kind of amusement. It would have been difficult for any human being to project a clearer sense of total unconcern.

"Aggie," her mother said, "this is Karen."

"Hi. Nice to meet you," Karen said, and stuck out a hand.

Aggie looked out at the proffered hand, did nothing. Karen showed no sign of any adverse reaction. "Aggie is a pretty name," Karen said. "Is it short for anything? Agatha?" No response. "Agoraphobia?"

That bought Karen a flicker of Aggie's eyes: a look that said, *What? What kind of nuthatch did you come out of?*

Karen simply smiled. "Hey, I've got an idea. Want to show me your room?"

"Now, that's a good idea," Joe said. "Go on, Aggie. Show her."

With the air of a child who knows that something bad is going to happen no matter what she does, Aggie turned and headed for the stairs. Karen went after her, glancing reassuringly at Joe and Leslie. They looked after her, then exchanged a glance. Maybe, just maybe, it would work. . . .

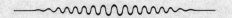

The room was fairly neat for a ten year old's. There was a handsome big dollhouse in one corner; various stuffed animals lay around here and there. Aggie slouched in, all her body language saying "I don't care if you're here, I'd just as soon you were gone," and slumped down on the bed.

"This is pretty," Karen said, looking around the room. "Hey, what a cool bed! Do you ever bounce on it?" She sat down on the bed, not too far from Aggie, but not too close, either. "I used to love to do that when I was your age. I bet you could bounce all the way up to the ceiling."

Aggie rolled her eyes and continued to do the best she could to ignore Karen, but Karen was being too good-natured for the rudeness to take. She glanced around, and her eyes fell on the clown doll that Aggie offhandedly picked up and held. "Hey—I used to have a clown just like that when I was your age. Can I see her?"

Aggie clutched the clown close; this was asking for a bit too much. She gave the intrusive woman a look that said, "Who the hell do you think you are?" But still Karen wore that easygoing smile, and it just didn't seem to go away—which surprised Aggie: usually adults didn't waste this much patience on her.

"Please?" Karen said. "I'll show you something your clown can do that I bet you didn't know about."

Oh, go on, Aggie thought. *Maybe after that you'll get out of my face.* She handed the clown over.

Karen took the clown, and with one hand behind it, worked its arms so that it covered its face with its "hands," then waved at Aggie. "Hello, Aggie," Karen said, faking a voice for the clown. "Do you like our new friend, Karen? I sure do." She then made the clown "give" her a large kiss. Disgusted, Aggie looked away, thinking, *I don't believe this. . . .*

Two-handed, Karen made the clown do a fairly pathetic jive-dance on the nearby dresser with background music. Aggie viewed this performance with colossal scorn, and said, "You must think I'm about five."

Karen gave her a thoughtful look. "Can you make her dance like this?"

"Yes. It's no big deal."

Karen perched the clown back up on the dresser, then reached down to her collar to touch something that Aggie just noticed for the first time: a long, slender crystal on a pendant. She held it, then looked at the clown.

Aggie looked at it too, more out of reflex than anything else. The air suddenly buzzed oddly . . . and to her complete astonishment, the clown doll began to move. It spread its arms, stood up slowly on the dresser, and started to dance, *by itself*. Nothing touched it. Nothing came near it.

Aggie stared at the clown, then at Karen. She leapt up off the bed, and fled.

"Aggie?" Karen said, and went after her hurriedly.

Aggie shut herself in the bathroom, braced herself up against the wall by the sink. The bathroom was clean again, now, but too clearly she could see in her mind the way it had been, and she could hear again the long sighs and occasional angry muttering that had come out of it as, first her mother, then her father, had busied themselves cleaning the place. That had been bad enough. But now this! The clown had suddenly become an echo of what had happened before: the sense of fear, of loss of control. And it was worse still, this time, because she knew it wasn't her fault. Someone *else* had done it.

The thought was terrifying—and at the same time, something about it tempted her. *Someone else. . . .*

Outside the door, Karen knocked. "Aggie . . . open the door, please."

"Go away!"

But she didn't. And Aggie felt something in the air, like a stirring. She had felt it the other night, when looking into the mirror, and when Karen had made the clown dance, and in the playground. . . . That same tingling; that buzz. She squeezed her eyes shut again in fear.

The door handle turned, forcing its way around. The bolt inside the lock mechanism clicked a couple of times, then undid itself. The door swung open, to reveal Karen, standing there, quite untroubled, holding the clown.

Aggie didn't want to look at her. "Aggie . . ." Karen said.

"Go *away.*"

Karen stepped into the bathroom. "Did I scare you, Aggie?"

She winced and grabbed the clown away from Karen, not saying anything.

"If I scared you, I'm sorry. I didn't mean to. I only meant to show you what I can do."

Aggie looked at Karen suspiciously. "Why?"

"I think you know why, Aggie."

Against Aggie's will, interest was beginning to kindle in her. "No, I don't."

"You're just like me, Aggie. You can do the same things."

This suggestion was too bitter to let stand; Aggie had learned quickly enough from the kids at school that she had no kinship with them, and probably not with anyone else on Earth, either . . . at least, that was what they insisted. And her parents' insistence otherwise didn't matter, when they thought to give it: they were stuck with her . . . they had to say things like that. "No, I can't," Aggie said angrily. "I'm not like anybody."

"Yes, you are, Aggie."

Karen came a little closer. The smile she wore had faded a little, but that same sense of purpose, of certainty, still hung around her, and something else: a sense of clear recognition. Aggie knew that Karen understood this problem from the inside—the message was as clear as the "newsprint" about Clark's intentions had been. "Things just happen on their own when you're around, right?" Karen said. "And people don't like you because of it."

This was the suspicion which Aggie had been resisting most violently for the longest time, the truth she had thought would never *become* true if she could just keep from believing it herself. "I don't make things happen."

"I can teach you to control that power, Aggie. If you give me the chance."

The thought tantalized her—then Aggie thrust it away in horror. "I don't want to control it. I want it to go away!"

Aggie fled again, running down the hallway, making for the stairs, and downstairs.

Karen followed her.

———~~~∿∿∿∿∿∿∿∿∿~~~———

Down in the living room, Aggie plumped herself down in the chair under the front window, trying as hard as she could to look as if nothing out of the ordinary had happened. Her mother came over to her with an expression of concern. "Is everything all right, honey?"

"Everything's fine," Karen said, coming out of the downstairs hallway. "I think Aggie and I will get along just great."

Aggie's mother and father looked at each other, an expression no longer entirely hopeless; then her father hunkered down beside her. "What do you think, Aggie? Would you like to have Karen come and stay with us?"

Aggie sat and thought silently, not looking at any of them. She had the horrible feeling once again that, once this woman was in here, she would never be able to get rid of her. *If it's not this one, it'll be another,* she thought. *They're going to stick me with someone like this no matter what I do.*

Aggie ventured the briefest glance up at Karen. *Then again . . . one like this . . . not just some ordinary person . . .*

. . . who knows? Something good might happen.

Oh, if only! . . .

But what if it doesn't? . . .

"Honey?" her father said. "It's up to you. Do you want Karen to stay?"

Aggie delayed the moment as long as she could . . . but it couldn't be put off for ever. Reluctantly, she looked up at her mother. "I guess."

Aggie's mother and father looked at each other again, more in amazement than anything else. Then Joe stuck a hand out to Karen. "Well then. Looks like you have a job."

"Excellent!" she said, shaking his hand happily. Karen glanced down at Aggie; after a moment, Aggie looked up again, still holding the clown tight. It was dangerous, so dangerous, to start having hope that anything would change. But still . . . it was hard, so hard to resist. . . .

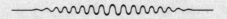

In another town, in another street, stood one small home among many: another typical American heartland home . . . except this one had a terrible ache at its heart.

Inside, a mother and father sat on the living room couch. The mother's eyes were red: they showed signs of having been that way for a long time. Occasionally she would glance over at the framed photo of a young girl on a nearby table.

Across from the couch stood a bearded man with a face that might have been kindly, had there not been such a fierce and driven quality about it. He said, "And how long has she been missing, Mr. Hagen?"

"Three weeks." Mr. Hagen looked up at the questioner with an expression full of grief, but also of annoyance. "We already went through this with the police. . . . I would think you people would have better things to do than question us over and over."

"Our agency likes to conduct its own investigation," said the bearded man calmly. Plainly he was not going to go away; the father sighed.

"What agency did you say you were with? The FBI?"

"No, sir. My agency has a slightly narrower focus than the FBI. We concentrate on missing children like Lucy."

At the sound of her daughter's name, the woman looked down at the picture on the table again . . . then further down still. She had found out over the last few weeks that this was the best way to cry without it being utterly obvious. "Well," she said, "she was walking home from school. People saw her leaving the playground and walking to the bus stop. And then . . . she was just gone."

The bearded man took a notebook out of his pocket, began to write. "She'd never take a ride from somebody she didn't know," Lucy's mother said. "Lucy has too much common sense for that."

"Is it possible she was picked up by your nanny? Martha?"

Lucy's mother shook her head. "Martha wasn't in town. A few weeks before Lucy disappeared she had a family emergency and had to go to Florida. . . ."

Lucy's father looked at the bearded man. "You don't think Martha had something to do with this?"

The man's closed face made it obvious that he did. "Oh, my God—" Lucy's mother said.

The bearded man stood, went through his notebook for a moment, then came up with a photograph, which he handed to Lucy's mother and father. "Is this a photo of Martha?"

The photo showed a young woman with short dark hair, a wide, cheerful mouth, wearing a smile that seemed not to want to go away. "Yes," Lucy's father said softly.

Lucy's mother shook her head. "*She* couldn't have anything to do with . . . she *loved* Lucy. . . ."

The man looked at them with some pity, but his face was still hard, and something eager was showing in it now. "Tell me anything you can about 'Martha.'"

Lucy's mother spread her hands helplessly. "She was new in town, so she didn't have many friends."

"She said something about being an only child—maybe that was part of it," Lucy's father said. "Keeping to herself, that is. She spent most of her time with Lucy."

The bearded man sighed, made another note in his notebook, then looked up again. "Do you have any records that concern Martha? Social security forms, resumés, a phone bill? Anything that might tell me where to find her?"

Lucy's mother and father looked at each other blankly, shook their heads. Then Lucy's mother looked thoughtful, and said, "Well, there was one thing. She used to get . . . packages. I don't know if they were from home. I bring in the mail every day, and I couldn't help noticing. . . ."

The bearded man glanced up. "Do you remember the address?"

Lucy's mother thought. "The name, yes. . . . 'Anti—'" She paused, looked at her husband; he couldn't help. "Antiquarius Books?"

"In what city?" asked the bearded man.

Lucy's mother shook her head. "I can't remember. Just—the name stuck in my head: it seemed a little unusual."

She sighed. Her husband was shaking his head again. "I can't believe it, though," he said. "They were like sisters, practically—Lucy and Martha."

The bearded man looked up again. "Did Martha ever give Lucy anything . . . a gift . . . maybe a small crystal?"

Lucy's mother and father both looked up sharply at that. "Yeah," her father said, "she gave her the prettiest little crystal. Lucy loved it. How did you know about that?"

The bearded man shook his head, closed his notebook, and put it away. "Well," he said, "this has been a good start. Thank you very much."

He got up, looking gravely at Lucy's mother and father. "Do you think you're going to find Lucy?" her mother said, very quietly.

The bearded man sighed. "If it's not too late. . . ."

———∿∿∿∿∿∿∿∿∿∿∿———

He got into his car, picked up the cellphone and hit one of the speed-dial buttons. "This is Walsh. Patch me to Selma."

A soft squeaking came from the phone. "Yeah, Selma. I think I may have a lead." He glanced at the notebook again. "I need a location on an Antiquarius Books, somewhere in the continental U.S. When I've got that, I'll need a plane—and a car."

Another moment's squeaking. "I don't care how many there are," Walsh said, rather wearily, "I'll check them all. . . . Right. Bye." He hung up, drove off, his eyes filling again with the determination that kept him going.

He was getting closer. This time . . . *this* time he would find her. And when he did, this festering sore of a problem would be lanced once and for all. No more little girls hurt by these people. No more of the pain caused by watching what had to be done to the children afterwards. No more interference by the government in families' relationships with their daughters . . . and no more interference from these people, either. Terry Walsh would find himself out of a job . . . and be one of the happiest people on the planet.

———————~~~wwwwwwwww~~~———————

In Antiquarius Books, the phone rang, and the gray-haired woman picked it up. "Antiquarius Books, this is Jean. . . ."

"Hi," said a familiar voice, over a background of muted street noise: the caller was using a pay phone. "It's me. I just wanted you to know . . . I've made contact, and we definitely have a positive. A little girl named Aggie Travis."

Jean sat down quietly, reassured at the sound of Karen's voice. It had been too long since she'd last heard from her. "Good. How soon will she be ready?"

"I don't know yet. The mother is suspicious. But I'm already in and working on it. It won't be long. . . ."

Karen hung up, and Jean turned her attention back to her desk. *If we can just save one more,* she thought. *One more.* . . . Every one saved, every one brought out of the stifling environments into a secure place where she could be herself and reach her own full potential, whatever that might be . . . every one was a victory.

Jean had no idea how long she would be spared for such victories. She had no illusions that her part in this battle would last all that much longer, or that she would have the leisure to die in bed. The sheer juggernaut inertia of her pursuers was making that ever more unlikely. But if they thought that realization was likely to stop her, They, the government, were very confused indeed. And when she at last fell out of the picture, others would step in to replace her. Others were already doing so.

"Karen . . ." she breathed, and picked up another newspaper.

————~~~~~~~~~———

The sun came in brightly through the windows of Aggie's bedroom. Karen stepped in, wandered over to one of the windows and gazed out. Aggie was sitting on the bed, reading and trying her best to look completely uninterested. It was, admittedly, something of a job.

Karen idly gave a spin to the toy merry-go-round sitting on the windowsill, and said, "So, Aggie, what do you like to do? Do you have any friends?"

Aggie could have laughed out loud at that. "Nobody wants to be friends with me."

"I do."

"My parents pay you," Aggie said bitterly.

Karen shrugged a little. "That doesn't mean I can't be your friend. Does it?"

Aggie let this imponderable slip by, since she had never heard anything quite like it before. Karen wandered over and sat down on the bed, again not too close, and said softly, "I used to get those headaches, too."

Aggie looked up in surprise, interested even though she had been trying hard not to be, and closed the book she had been "reading," pushing it aside. "You did?"

"Yep. Whenever I got mad. And sometimes I could see this glow around people. And if I squeezed it down tight . . . things would happen to them."

It was too terrible . . . too hard to believe. Aggie almost didn't want to hear Karen saying it, even though they were alone, with no one else to hear. But, oh, to feel that there was someone else, even *one* someone. . . . "Glow" wasn't exactly the word Aggie would have chosen, but it sounded similar enough to what she saw when the air began to hum and buzz, when things started to happen. . . . "You were like me when you were little?"

Karen nodded. "You're not alone, Aggie."

She turned. Over on the nearby dresser, where the clown had sat and danced the other day, was a glass of water with a straw in it. "Look at this straw . . ." Karen said. She took hold of the little crystal she wore about her neck, then gazed thoughtfully at the straw.

The air tingled. The straw trembled . . . then stood straight upright in the middle of the glass, unsupported.

Aggie stared. The clown could have been a one-off—a trick. But not *this*. She had put the water and the straw there herself, that morning. And there was no question of it being accidental, just something that happened. Karen had *done* it. The air was still buzzing with whatever she had done.

"How did you do that?" Aggie breathed.

Karen breathed out. "I focused. I squeezed the light down to a point. You can focus, too."

This was something that Aggie had tried once or twice, with no results whatsoever. "No," she said, "it gets all goofed up when I do it."

"It doesn't have to," Karen said. She fished around in her pocket for a moment, then held something out to Aggie. "This will help you to focus."

Aggie took what Karen offered her. It was a long silvery chain with a slim clear crystal at the end of it. "A lot like mine," Karen said, glancing down at her own.

Bemused, Aggie slipped the chain on over her neck, resettled her pony tail. "Now," Karen said to her, "think about the straw."

Aggie glanced at the straw—then looked away, wincing a little at the first touch of the odd tingling feeling in the air. She tried it again—shied away again. Nothing happened.

"I can't do it," she said, frowning. Yet another false hope.

"Yes, you can," Karen said quickly. "Don't get mad. Really concentrate."

Aggie clutched the crystal, looked at the straw. That tingling seemed to build in the air again: a subdued buzzing, like bees. But this time, unlike the time in the bathroom, the buzzing sounded less threatening, almost friendly: as if it were under control—her control. *Impossible,* she thought, *don't believe it, it's not real.* But Karen was still watching her. To prove her wrong, if nothing else, Aggie kept looking at the straw, thinking about it. *Stand up straight*—

It wobbled, then fell off to the side of the glass again.

She turned to Karen, ready to complain angrily about being tricked, but Karen wasn't having any of

it. "Once more," she said. "I want you to really concentrate. Shut everything out but the straw."

Aggie narrowed her eyes, clutched the crystal
harder, and stared at the straw as she had stared at
Clark in the playground the other day, as she had
stared at so many other kids, over the years, to no
effect. *Come on. Up. Straight up—*

The straw wobbled again—and stood straight in
the glass, without help.

Am I sure. . . . She glanced sideways at Karen.
"You're doing that."

Karen wasn't touching her crystal, though. She
shook her head, watching the straw with a connois-
seur's eye. "No, *you're* doing that."

Delighted, Aggie turned her attention back to the
straw. It wiggled—then shot straight up into the air, out
of the glass and over the bed, raining on them in a tiny
way as it passed over and came down on the far side.

They both laughed. Aggie was utterly astounded,
both at the exhilaration of doing something right for
a change, and of doing something so cool and
strange. She reached out to Karen and gave her a
quick hug, which Karen returned with as much pleasure. That was the astonishing thing: Aggie could
read her intentions and feelings, again, as clearly as
she had read Clark's nasty ones the other day.

Then Aggie sat back, suddenly as winded as if she'd
run from one side of the playground to the other without any preparation. "Wow," she said. She looked up at
Karen, wondering if it was safe to ask the question . . .
but her curiosity got the better of her in short order.
"Did you hurt people when you got mad?" Aggie said.

Karen nodded. "I did until I learned to control it."

Aggie frowned. "I don't want to control it. When people are mean to me, I want them to get hurt!"

Karen nodded—looking, Aggie thought, a little sad. From somewhere in Karen's background "noise," Aggie heard/felt a wash of regret for someone hurt in the old days—Aggie couldn't make out any concrete details, but it still made Karen mad at herself even now. "I know," she said, "but that's not right, Aggie. We don't use our special powers to hurt people."

"Why not?"

"Because we don't."

Aggie blinked—she was more used to being given elaborate and suspect-sounding reasons, rather than simple flat negatives.

Karen said, very firmly, "That's not why nature gives us these special powers. Besides, once you learn to focus, people won't be mean to you as often."

Aggie blinked at that thought. Her universe had never before included the idea of a place where people were *not* routinely mean to her. Karen looked understanding. "We'll practice," she said, "every day. The two of us."

Aggie looked at her and wondered, for the first time with real hope, whether everything might not be about to turn out all right after all. . . .

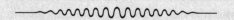

In Antiquarius Books, Jean was ranging up and down the shelves of one aisle, looking for the new edition of

Childhood's End which she knew was hiding there somewhere; some well-meaning browser had mis-shelved it, probably. From behind her, a male voice said, "Excuse me, do you have any books on the human genome project?"

She glanced over her shoulder at him: a big bearded man, with intent eyes. "I'll see. . . ." She looked up and down the shelf, frowning a little, as much at the lack of any recommendation as from the slow subtle tingling along her nerves, a feeling that his presence here wasn't merely about books. "I don't believe we have any general books on the subject," she said.

"Thank you." The man paused a moment, then said, "That's a very interesting crystal you're wearing. Where would I get something like that?"

Jean turned to look at him full face for the first time, feigning complete unconcern, though the tingling along her nerves was getting stronger. "It's one of a kind," she said casually.

"Oh," said the bearded man, "I'm sure I've seen crystals exactly like that . . . Jean."

She blinked. It was important, even now, not to seem too surprised. . . . "Who *are* you?"

"Just a man with questions, Jean. For example . . . where's Lucy Hagen? Or a nanny named Martha? Where are they hiding? I think you know the answers."

She backed away from him nervously. *It's* Them. *Oh, God—not here, not now, not so soon!* The tingling along her nerves was turning to a buzz of alarm as he reached out to her, grabbed her by the shoulders. "Tell me—"

Jean cried out, "No!"

And her partner, the bookstore's owner, came bustling down the aisle, brushing between her and the man. "Jean," she said, looking at him with a frown, "should I call the police?"

"No, don't bother," the man said coolly, and turned and walked away, heading out of the shop.

"Jean," her partner said, seeing Jean flush and then go pale with sudden fear, "what can I do?"

Jean shook her head. *Have they bugged the place already?* she wondered. *Are the phones safe? Who knows how long they might have been listening.* Jean looked Carol in the eye, and said, "Don't worry. Just tell everyone . . . I'll be gone for a few days."

She walked away, leaving the other woman looking after her anxiously. But there was nothing she could do about that just now . . . and a lot more that needed to be done. . . .

———~~~~~~~———

Around the corner, Walsh was on the phone to someone in his office. "I found her," he said, almost in triumph. "Face to face with the famous Jean Anderson, which is what she's calling herself these days."

The phone squeaked a question. "No, I didn't have her picked up," he said. "No point in it. She's over fifty; her powers are so diminished, she's no threat. But she will lead us to the others. Maybe even to Sanctuary itself."

More soft squeaking. "Right. Well, it shouldn't take much longer. Here's what I want you to do. . . ."

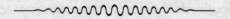

Leslie walked in the front door, shut it behind her, dropped her bag on the table, and looked around. "Aggie?" she said.

No answer. She walked down toward the kitchen. "Aggie?"

They should be back by now, she thought . . . and her heart seized. Even now, now that things had seemed to actually start going well, Leslie couldn't get rid of the idea that something disastrous was going to happen, that something— "Aggie," she said, suddenly and irrationally frightened, making for the kitchen and raising her voice, "are you here?"

Then the key turned in the front door lock, and the door opened. Aggie and Karen were standing there. Aggie was holding a pink balloon, and looking positively radiant. "Hi," Karen said to Aggie's mother.

Still flustered, Leslie said, "I just got home—I didn't see anybody. You should have left a note."

"I did." Karen slipped out of her coat, hung it up on the nearby coat hook. "I left it in the kitchen. I said we were going to the park and we'd be back by—" She checked her watch. "—now. Is that okay?"

Leslie tried to get hold of herself again. It was surprisingly hard. "That's fine," she said. "Fine."

Aggie, too, was slipping out of her coat. "Did you have fun?" her mother said.

"I guess," Aggie said, blandly.

Leslie blinked a little. Was something being hidden from her? Or was this just the kid-thing of wanting to die a horrible death before your parents see you demonstrating wholehearted enthusiasm about *anything?* "You guess?" she said. "Well, that's better than 'no'."

Aggie unbent so far as to grin a little. She slipped over to her mother and said in an undertone, as if it was to be kept strictly secret, "I really *like* Karen."

Leslie blinked in surprise: this was not something she had expected to hear, certainly not at this early stage. Aggie tended to keep her own counsel for prolonged periods, as if uncomfortable with what her parents' reaction to some opinion might be until she had held that opinion herself for a long time. "Do you? Well, that's great. Go wash up, okay?"

Aggie nodded, perfectly sunnily, and ran upstairs to do it.

Leslie watched her go, shaking her head slightly, and then said to Karen, "I think she likes you. You must have some kind of magic."

Karen just smiled . . . and Aggie's mother, for some reason, felt the fear start up again. She turned hurriedly and went off to make herself a cup of tea.

Karen watched. . . .

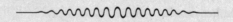

Leslie was straightening up a few things in the upstairs hall when Joe presented himself behind her, grabbed her, and began to tickle her in a way that he hadn't for a long time. She swung around, chuckling a little, and realized at the same time, guiltily, that she hadn't laughed with such pleasure for a while, either. The guilt had to do with the fact that she still wasn't happy about this whole situation, and she couldn't really tell why. . . .

To her husband, though, Leslie said, "*Someone* came home in a good mood."

"I'm happy," Joe said, straightforward and unconcerned. "I'm happy because Aggie's happy. I haven't seen her like this in a long time. It worked."

"What worked?"

"Karen."

Leslie wished she could be completely certain about that. Joe caught the uncertain expression that crossed Leslie's face. "Don't you like her?" Joe said.

"I like her," said Leslie. "It's just . . . she's just . . . too *perfect*. Don't you think? I mean, if Karen's so good, why hasn't she stayed with another family for a long time?"

Joe blinked at her. "She did, those people in Hawaii. Didn't you call them?"

"Yes," Leslie said. "I spoke to the mother. Her name was . . . Jean."

"And what did Jean say?"

Leslie looked rueful at her own unwillingness to accept something that was working out, something that had made her husband so happy. "Well, to listen to her . . . Karen is heaven-sent."

"Then there you have it. Accept it. We got lucky. For once."

He hugged her again, let her go and went off to change out of his work clothes. Aggie's mother looked after him . . . concerned, and unable to say anything concrete about *why*.

Halfway across town, in the street, Karen walked slowly over to the tall, gray-haired woman in the dark trench coat. "Jean—"

They hugged, then began to walk. "I came as soon as I could," Karen said. "What are you doing here?"

"It's the trackers," Jean said, grim. "They found me."

"Oh, no!" Karen went pale. "Why didn't they grab you?"

"I don't know, but I came to warn you: it may not be long before he finds where I'm hiding . . . and before he finds you and Aggie."

Karen swallowed.

"How is she?" Jean said.

Karen shook her head at the unfairness of life, for she knew what Jean was going to say next. "Jean . . . she's the best I've ever seen. Her powers are still unfocused, but she's strong. Stronger than I was, stronger than anyone I've ever seen. . . . She's got the inner sense, the 'underhearing' that only a few of us have ever had."

"Well, then, we don't have a moment to waste." Jean frowned. "We have to take her before the tracker gets here."

"She's nowhere near ready," Karen said.

"We can't be concerned with that now," said Jean. "Bring her to me."

Karen shook her head again. "But she hasn't found her inner peace. . . ." And that was so important, she knew: until you finally settled into acceptance of the gift, it would continue to act up at bad moments, never really falling properly under your control . . . and leaving you more a loose cannon on the deck of life than a weapon which could be used in other people's behalf. She couldn't bear the idea that Aggie might fall foul of such a fate with her abilities: not now, not when it was so little time at issue. . . . "Just give me a little more time, a couple more days. If we take her now, she'll never really trust us."

It was Jean's turn, now, to shake her head. "If that tracker finds us," she said, "it's the camp for her and God knows what for you and me. I know we have rules, but I'll break them all to save one little girl from their experiments."

Karen sighed. "I know. I'm sorry. I only meant. . . ."

"I'll give you two days. Forty-eight hours. Then I want her."

"Thank you." Karen had no idea whether it was going to be enough time . . . she was afraid it might not be. But she would do what she could, anything she could . . . and forty-eight hours from now was infinitely better than right this minute.

Jean nodded. "Keep your eyes open," she said.

"Where will you be?"

"Watching."

Jean walked away briskly, leaving Karen standing in the street, feeling suddenly cold.

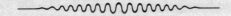

Karen climbed the stairs to Aggie's room, wondering what to do now.

This was, in her experience, the most dangerous part of the whole process: the most delicately balanced part, when a breath of wind or a misplaced thought could destroy days, even weeks of work. Karen looked back, now, almost wistfully, to the old days when you might have as long as six months with a little girl, maybe even a year. Now, with the authorities close on all their trails, it was a matter of weeks . . . sometimes days, like this case.

She's not a case, Karen told herself severely. *She's a child.* She had been a case once, herself, far back in the bad old days when child psychologists were likely to diagnose any obscure or inexplicable behavior as either "delinquency" or "retardation." And she had met many others who were designated "cases," unjustly so. She remembered in particular one little girl who had been diagnosed as a genuine "idiot," in the days when they still used such terms, because she wouldn't learn to read. It wasn't dyslexia, either; because of lack of money, she had been taught at home, by her mother . . . who also had the Gift. The little girl hadn't seen the need to learn to read black blotches on the page, when her mother could look at a book, and make the pictures seem to come alive. Who needs the words "they sailed the boat," this little girl said, when you could see the water spanking along the boat's side, the sails filling, feel the wind, hear the water and feel the spray on your skin? . . .

That little girl was now a mother herself, teaching other little girls, and her mother was with her; the two of them were one of the great treasures in Karen's life. She reminded herself once again that it was not just Aggie she had to be concerned about: it was them as well. If she lingered here too long over Aggie's trouble, they would be in danger too. . . .

Karen walked into Aggie's bedroom to find about six of the stuffed animals performing a stately and elegant minuet in the air over Aggie's bed. They dropped to the bed as Karen shut the door behind her. Aggie was lying there propped up on a pillow, looking comfortable, holding her crystal.

"You're getting really good," Karen said, walking around and doing some idle tidying of the room.

"I get kind of tired," said Aggie, "but it's really fun. I can't wait to show Mommy and Daddy."

"Aggie . . ." Karen paused, then came to sit on her bed, and patted one of Aggie's legs, trying not to look too conspiratorial; this was not something you could frame as a game . . . or, if you did, you were likely to get in trouble later. "You really *can't* show Mommy and Daddy. The power we have is a big secret. The biggest secret ever."

"Why?" Aggie said.

Karen sighed. "Because even grown-ups—even mommies and daddies—act like those kids at school. They think that we can make them do things, and they can't stop us. It makes them afraid, and sometimes it makes them mean. You know what I'm talking about."

Aggie frowned at that: it was clearly a concept she understood all too well. "I don't want to be around mean people."

Karen looked at Aggie, took a deep breath. This was the crucial part. "What if I told you there was a place? . . . A special place where there were other little girls just like you? It's where I live, and it's called Sanctuary."

Aggie looked at her with interest. "Is it a town?"

"Sometimes we're in a town. Sanctuary's really more of a group. We move around, to stay safe from bad people. We teach each other, and protect each other . . . and when we're ready, we go out and find more girls who need us." She leaned a little closer, and said, "Would you like to go there with me?"

Aggie considered it. "Can I take my parents?"

"No, Aggie. Sanctuary isn't for them."

Aggie considered that too . . . then said, quite casually, but with certainty, "Then it's not for me, either." She turned away dismissively.

Karen glanced sideways as she thought of the trackers . . . of Jean, and what Jean was likely to say about all this. So far, things had been fairly straightforward. But they would not be for long. . . .

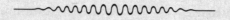

Elsewhere in town, Walsh was in his car, on the cellphone. His free hand was busy with delicate adjustments to the top of a "black box" sitting in the passenger's seat next to him. "All right," he was saying to the person on the other end, "I'm getting a good directional signal. You take the van down Fourteenth. If you get a fix, we'll finally be able to triangulate."

After a moment, he nodded, hung up, and began to drive.

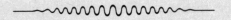

That afternoon, in the park, another game of kickball was going on. Karen was standing on the sidelines with Aggie. A ball came flying at Aggie: she caught it just before it hit her, but not before it brushed her face. Her eyes narrowed. A voice yelled, "Sorry!"

Aggie stared at the source of the ball, the young boy who had kicked it. "Throw it back, please," he said.

Aggie glared. Karen, though, put her hand lightly on Aggie's shoulder. "Aggie," she said softly, "control."

Aggie paused for a moment, then the angry look passed, and she threw the ball back. "Thank you," said the kid, and after a moment, Aggie actually threw him a small smile.

Karen strolled away, sat down on a bench next to Aggie's parents. Aggie's mother leaned over to her, and said, "I've been watching Aggie, and much as I hate to admit it, she's *much* better. You're a miracle worker, Karen."

"No," Karen said, a little guiltily. "I was just in the right place at the right time. She's just outgrowing her problems."

They all watched her for a second. Then Karen became aware of the pressure of someone's regard: turned, and saw the shadow of a gray trench coat over in the bushes. "Excuse me," she said to Aggie's parents. "Little girls' room."

She got up and headed for the little rest-room building: then slipped around it and came out on the other side, where Jean was standing, looking even grimmer than usual. They strolled together out into the green field on the other side of the building. "Jean," Karen said, almost afraid to ask, "what are you doing here?"

"I told you I'd be watching." Jean looked disappointed, and threw a glance back in the direction of the playing field, and Aggie. "She's still got a lot of anger. You haven't made progress since the last time I saw her. We need to go to Sanctuary."

"She doesn't want to go," Karen said. She had been trying all afternoon to find a gentle way to break this to Jean: there was none.

"I'm afraid, with the trackers this close," Jean said, "we can't wait any longer."

"And to hell with our rules!" Karen said.

Jean sighed, and walked a little way in silence, her face showing profound regret. "The year before I rescued you," she said, "I found this little girl in Modesto, California. Joy was her name. So smart, so pretty. She was a little ballerina . . . she was able to focus enough so that she could almost fly."

Jean's face softened, though Karen got a feeling that this would at best be temporary. "Joy loved her parents," Jean said, "and I was young. I couldn't see why I should take her away from them, so I didn't."

Her face hardened as they stopped for a moment; Karen glanced away. "I saw her years later, after they'd finished testing her at one of the camps. When they were done they 'neutralized' her, which is just a polite term for their kind of electroshock. She could barely walk, much less dance. They killed what made Joy special; and they did it without a second thought. 'National security.'"

Jean looked at Karen with an expression that made it plain she would brook no further denials. "I'll be waiting at the Burrard Motor Inn," she said, "at the corner of Burrard and Third. Room 23."

She walked off, leaving Karen feeling as grim and cold as Jean had looked.

Now *what do I do?* . . .

Late afternoon was slanting across the park as the family walked out, looking very much like the American dream: mother, father, intelligent young daughter, doting nanny. "Well," Joe said, "this has been fun!"

"It still *is* fun. Let's stay and have it be some *more* fun!" Aggie said.

"Nope, that's enough for today, hon," said her mother. "Come on, Aggie, let's get in the car."

Aggie bounced around, unwilling to take the first "no" for an answer . . . or the second, or third. "Can't we stay here a little longer? Please!"

"No, honey," her dad said. "We've been here long enough. We'll come back next week."

"Aren't you tired?" said her mother, slightly amazed, as usual, at the boundless energy of the young, at least when they were happy.

"No."

"All that sugar," her mother sighed.

"I have an idea," said Karen. "You two go on ahead . . . Aggie and I will walk back. Burn off some of this energy."

"Yeah! Can we, Mommy? Please!"

Smiling, Aggie's mother glanced at Joe, then nodded. "Sure. Sounds like a good idea."

"We'll see you at the house in about an hour?"

"You got it."

The two of them raced off: Aggie in the lead, Karen carrying a little more weight but quickly making up the distance in the back stretch. Relieved, Aggie's mother and father headed for the car.

~~~~~~~~~~~~~~~~

The motor inn was not too expensive and not too fancy, reworked from the concrete minimalism of the fifties, but not enough to make it unaffordable for more modern travelers. Jean unlocked the door, and walked in with a brown paper bag of groceries, viewing the place with the equanimity of familiarity: cheap bedspread, plain walls, cheaply framed prints screwed to the walls, carpet tiles that had seen better days. She sighed, making for the kitchenette to put away the groceries. She wouldn't be here long enough to care much about the decor. There were more important issues. . . .

The voice came from one side, and caught her completely by surprise. "Hello, Jean."

She stopped dead, turned . . . and saw Walsh standing in the bathroom door, with the gun trained on her.

Did he find them? she thought instantly. *Oh, please don't let him have found them. . . .*

"Put the bag down," Walsh said. "Slowly."

She just looked at him for a moment. "You followed me from Parkview," she said.

"Actually," said Walsh, "I followed the transponder I planted in your purse the other day."

Jean nodded, matter-of-fact. She'd always known it was going to have to come to this. Now that it had come at last, she felt a peculiar sensation of pure relief. "Then where are the others?" Jean said. "The rest of the bureau-Nazis."

"They'll be here shortly," said Walsh. "Maybe you can make this much less unpleasant and simply tell me where Martha or Karen is. And who the next little girl is, too. What's her name? Where is she?"

Jean walked slowly past him with the groceries, into the kitchenette, where she began to unpack them. "I told you . . . I don't know what you're talking about."

Walsh planted himself behind her in the kitchenette doorway, blocking any possible escape. "We're going to find out, Jean. I predict that by the end of the day we will have your assistant kidnapper and the little girl, and one other thing: the location of Sanctuary. We're going to have all of you in the camp by the end of the week."

She looked over at him, turning away from the bag and folding her arms to lean against the counter.

"Generations of women have been hunted and hounded by men like you," Jean said. "You called us witches—burned us at the stake. I've seen my friends taken away and 'neutralized,' all because we could do things that you couldn't. You're all so afraid you're going to be replaced, like the Neanderthals. Well . . . from the way you've acted, you *deserve* to be replaced. There are times when I've wished we were capable of fighting back, but that's not our way."

Walsh lifted the gun a little, looking at her thoughtfully. She regarded it with disdain. "I'm not afraid of that," Jean said, quite calm. "I'll die before I'll tell you anything."

"Oh, you're not going to die, Jean," said Walsh, with great satisfaction, and tucked the gun away. "But you *are* going to do a lot of talking."

Jean looked at him, the fear showing in her eyes for the first time . . . then went back to unpacking the groceries.

———~~~^^^vvv^^^vvv^^^~~~———

In the park, Karen and Aggie walked by the little stream that ran down to the park's small lake. "Karen . . ." Aggie said. "How come I can do things?"

Karen smiled a bit, for this was one part of the explanations that she always enjoyed. "You have something called a Z chromosome. It's something that only women can have, and not very many of them . . . maybe one in a million. It's sort of a key to . . . being able to focus."

They stepped up onto the bridge over the little stream, pausing to look down at the water. "You have a Z chromosome, too, don't you?" Aggie said. "You can focus, too."

Karen nodded. "Yes. I'm not as strong as you, though. Strength varies from individual to individual. But generally, the older you get, the weaker your powers get."

Aggie shook her head at this, bemused. "How did it happen?"

They walked on. "We were just born this way," Karen said. "Some men have an extra Y chromosome. It's just nature trying something new. Maybe in five hundred years, everybody will have a Z."

Aggie frowned. "If it makes me so different, why can't they just take it out?"

"Well, it's too small to see, much less take out." They paused again, having come down off the bridge, and examined the paths leading away.

"How long are you gonna stay at our house?" Aggie said.

Karen's heart twinged a little. "We'll see."

"That's not a real answer," said Aggie.

Karen paused—then suddenly took Aggie's hand, leading her off to one side, to another path leading down from the bridge, and out toward the edge of the park. "Let's go over this way," she said. . . .

Jean watched the van pull up outside the motor inn. Walsh went to the window, spoke to his confederate briefly on the cellphone. "Just a few minutes . . . I'll have the information we need."

He didn't find them, Jean thought with profound relief, and swallowed. She headed calmly down to the bathroom, not rushing.

"Yeah, tell him that I said—"

Hearing a tinkle of breaking glass, Walsh turned suddenly, raced down to the bathroom.

He got there too late. Jean lay on the floor. Walsh bent over her, caught the bitter-almond smell of cyanide wafting up from her lips, saw the discoloration—

"Damnit!" He whipped the phone out again. "She's taken poison," he said. "And I didn't get the next girl's name!"

A pause, a soft squeaking from the phone. "No," he said. "Stay there a moment. There's something else we can do."

He moved over to the phone by the bed, squinted at it to see which number to dial for the front desk: punched it, and waited.

"Front desk? Do you keep records of calls made from the rooms?" A pause. "Good—I'll be right over."

———∿∿∿∿∿∿∿∿∿∿———

Aggie and Karen swung down the street in the low, long afternoon sunshine. "What are you gonna be when you grow up?" said Aggie.

Karen gave her an amused look. "I'm already grown up."

"No, when you're really, really old. Like thirty."

It's gone this far, Karen thought regretfully, *she's accepted me as an equal. Oh, why do things have to happen this way. . . .* She snickered a little at the ruthless definition of thirty as irrevocably over the hill, and then said, "I always wanted to help people. What do *you* want to be?"

"I want to be a mountain climber."

Karen smiled a little ruefully. "I don't think there's much money in that. . . ."

"Huh," Aggie said, giving her an ironic look.

"No," Karen said, putting an arm around the girl, "I know. You want to be alone. So did I. But you can't." She sighed, shook her head, remembering how tempting the empty places had been . . . until she had found another avocation. But more to the point, there just weren't enough empty places in the world. . . .

Aggie stopped suddenly. "This isn't the way home."

"I know," Karen said. "I just wanted to stop here real quick to see a friend. Is that okay?"

Aggie thought about it. "Okay," she said. "Where does she live? Is she nice? Are we almost there?"

Karen led Aggie down the street, halfway to heartbreak.

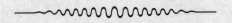

Karen knocked on the unprepossessing door of the motor inn. Aggie looked around her with interest, said nothing.

Karen knocked again. There was no reply.

The thought of the trackers, of the shadowy implacable forces which she knew had been getting closer and closer, drove Karen to do something she wouldn't normally have done out in the open. She lifted a hand to the crystal around her neck, took hold of it, and looked at the doorknob.

It turned, snapped around despite resistance; the bolt undid itself. The door swung open.

Karen and Aggie stood there a moment. Karen listened . . . the place was empty . . . but empty in some way she very much disliked. "Stay here a moment, Aggie," she said, and went in.

She looked around at the bed, neatly made: peered into the kitchen—saw a half-unpacked bag of groceries. "Jean?" she said.

Silence—the wrong kind.

"Jean?"

No answer. She walked down to the little bathroom—

—and gasped, and fell to her knees. A splinter of glass drove itself into Karen's knee; she ignored it.

The smell of bitter almonds filled the place: and the body seemed to, too, just left lying there, not cold yet—sprawled any old way on the cold floor, and empty, empty of what had made it most of value. Karen breathed hard, trying to think clearly. *They must have been here,* she thought. *They're probably very close to finding Aggie, too. And they would have found out about Sanctuary, too, except—*

The scream from behind her jolted her upright. Karen had just time enough to see Aggie's shocked face, see the little girl fleeing. *I've got to stop her!* She thought. *She'll run right into it—*

"Aggie! Come back here!"

But the little girl had already plunged out of the motel room, and slammed the door behind her. Karen could feel the buzzing beginning in the air, and knew all too well what was about to happen. She just managed to keep herself from touching the doorknob as it turned cherry-red and molten, slumping down against the door, which smoked and stank from contact with the molten metal.

Carefully avoiding the hot spot, Karen hammered desperately against the door. "Aggie!" she cried. "Wait! Let me explain—"

———∿∿∿∿∿∿∿∿∿———

The doorbell rang. Joe pulled the door open, to see a respectable-looking silver-bearded man in a suit and tie standing there. "Mr. and Mrs. Joseph Travis?"

"Yes?"

"Special Agent Walsh," he said, flashing a wallet badge at Joe. "I'm here about your daughter."

Joe opened his mouth, closed it again. This was completely beyond him. "She's out with her nanny. . . ." he said.

Leslie came up behind her husband. "Why?" she said, concerned. "Is something wrong?"

The man stepped in, bringing out a snapshot and showing it to them. "Is this the nanny? Is she named Martha?"

Joe and Leslie looked at each other. "That's a picture of Karen. . . ." Joe said.

"What has she done?" said Aggie's mother.

The man walked around their living room, pulling shades down. Joe and Leslie stared at him. "Did . . . Karen . . . give your child a gift?"

"Why, yes," Leslie said.

"Was it a crystal on a neck chain?"

"Yes!" Joe said. "How did you know that?"

Walsh looked grim. "My agency knows a great deal about this Karen. She kidnaps children."

"Kidnap?" Leslie and Joe looked at each other, and Joe immediately reached for his jacket. "I'm going to the park to find them. Stay here in case they come back."

But there was no need. The door flew open; Aggie burst in and ran to her mother, practically throwing herself at her. "Aggie!" Joe said.

"Aggie! Oh, my God, Aggie!" Leslie said. "Are you okay? You scared Mommy and Daddy to death—"

The bearded man moved in so smoothly, it was plain he had done this often before. He knelt down in front of Aggie, shouldering between her and Joe as if Joe wasn't even there, and said, pleasantly enough, "Hello, Aggie. My name is Terry. Can you tell me where Karen is?"

Aggie looked at him with sudden, profound suspicion, even through her obvious shock. "I left her at the other place."

The suspicion was instantly contagious. Leslie looked coldly at Walsh. "That's enough questions." She turned Aggie away, shooed her toward the stairs. "Aggie, go to your room and don't come down until I tell you."

Aggie started—but hesitated a third of the way up. "But who is he—"

"Never mind that. Aggie, go on! *Go*—"

She ran up the stairs. Walsh got up and tried to go after her: but he found himself suddenly staring right into Leslie's fierce eyes, and backed off. "I'm sorry," he said, "but I will need Aggie's help. Maybe when she's calmed down I could take her down to our office—" He began to pace, radiating a balked anger that wasn't used to being balked.

"She's not going *anywhere*," said Leslie, in the voice of a woman dealing with the unacceptable face of bureaucracy under her own roof.

"You don't realize how important this is!" Walsh said angrily.

"Oh, really?" said Joe, coming up behind Leslie. They glared at him together.

"There is a group of people in this country who are dangerous," Walsh said, like someone explaining politics to idiots. "My section finds them."

The tone didn't do much for Joe, or for Leslie. "And does what with them, exactly?" Leslie said. "I mean, *how* are they dangerous?"

"Because they're different." Walsh walked away, his face thunderous. "They prey on innocent little girls. They can't be controlled and they can't be stopped. They don't follow any rules—"

"Like the rules that let you hunt little girls like Aggie," said Karen, panting, from the open doorway.

Walsh turned and looked at her. Joe was surprised to see the expression of near-anxiety that crossed his face, interfering with the look of unmitigated anger and authority he had been wearing until then.

"Karen," Joe said, "what's this about?"

Karen advanced on Walsh. "There was this group of people in the government who studied women like me," she said. "Like Aggie. But some of them got afraid of what they found. They convinced themselves we were a *threat*—"

"You *are* a threat," Walsh said, reaching into his jacket, and coming out with his gun.

Karen simply looked at him, and took hold of her crystal. Her eyes narrowed slightly—

The air buzzed, as if with angry insects. Something, an invisible force like a wind made solid and angry, picked Walsh up and threw him, bodily, at a hanging tapestry on the nearby wall. He thudded into the wall, slid down it, and lay sprawled there, groaning softly.

The gun was no longer in his hand, but still within reach. Softly Karen made her way over to it, reached down—

Walsh's hand reached up, grabbed the crystal, and snapped its chain off Karen's neck. She staggered for a second—the second he needed; he got to his feet again, grabbed Karen from behind, and put the muzzle of the gun against her head.

She struggled, trying to get loose or to reach into the pocket where he had secreted the crystal, but it did no good. "See what I mean?" Walsh shouted.

"Why do you think I came back?" Karen said to the Travises. "I knew *he'd* be here. He's just killed the best friend I ever had! But I came anyway, because I care about Aggie."

"She's lying!" Walsh said.

"*One* of you is lying," said Joe, his eyes narrow.

"Leslie," Karen said urgently, "Aggie has the power to *do* things. It's something she was born with—"

"Shut up!" Walsh shouted, and threw the struggling Karen away from him. Her head hit the corner of a nearby bookshelf with a thump; Karen fell prone.

"No, *you* shut up," Joe said then, stepping forward, into the aim of the gun. "I think you're the one who's lying, Walsh."

"I'm trying to *save* us from them!" Walsh yelled at Joe. "We're on the same side and you're too stupid to realize it!"

Joe moved forward regardless. Walsh leveled the gun at him. Joe swallowed, and came on—

———————〜〜〜〜〜〜〜〜———————

Aggie heard the sounds from upstairs: the crashing, the voices raised in anger and despair. The air had been buzzing all around her ever since she looked over Karen's shoulder into the tacky little bathroom in the motor inn, and saw something she had seen a million times before on TV, but never in real life in anything bigger than a hamster: death. The sight of the blunt, everyday reality of it had tipped Aggie over into a new level of fear. It had been easy, then, to melt the motel room's doorknob, shutting herself safely away from the sad reality inside there on the bathroom floor. That she had shut Karen in with it as well didn't occur to her until she had run halfway home.

Most of the run home had been on autopilot. Aggie couldn't stop thinking how unnatural the body had looked, and how unreal, as if any minute the lady—Jean?—would get up and say, "It was all just a joke. . . ." But if this was a joke, it was a hugely unfair one, and it turned the world upside down for Aggie. She knew that grown-ups died . . . but not anywhere near *her*.

And now she ran home, to the place that should have been safe, and found her mother and father embedded in the stinging, buzzing air as if in amber, and talking to a stranger . . . whose mind smelled unmistakably of the weird almond smell that had been in the bathroom with the dead lady.

After being sent up to her room, Aggie had crouched on her bed for a minute or two while the voices were raised downstairs, afraid to go anywhere near that smell again. The air was buzzing more and more loudly, and she felt—*how* did she feel?—some-one else coming close, someone else who could hear the buzzing as well.

Aggie was scared, more scared than she had ever been. But this time there was something added—a sense that she might be able to *do* something. She already had done something, and something *real*—not like the kind of practice she had been doing with the stuffed toys.

The voices downstairs were getting louder. The front door thumped open. That presence which she had been feeling was here now. It felt familiar. There was a wide smile about it—

Aggie threw herself off her bed again and pounded down the stairs. Halfway down, she felt the crack of the bookcase against her, or rather Karen's, head; felt the liveness that was Karen suddenly go out, like a match dropped in water—

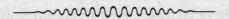

She spun herself around the bottom banister of the stairs out into the living room and took it all in, all in one glimpse: Karen collapsed on the ground, the bearded man, Walsh, leveling a gun at her father and mother. Walsh looked at her.

As she reached up to take hold of the crystal, their eyes locked.

She saw *into* him in a flash. Rage, rage and fear: blocking everything else that Aggie might have found out, lathered all over the top of his mind like the shaving cream all over the sink the other night. The rage moved with his glance to Karen. Aggie felt Walsh take the breath of preparation, getting ready to aim—

Not a chance, she thought: found the right spot, where those colorless flows came together like water going down the drain, and squeezed it. Walsh dropped the gun, screamed, clutched his head, and tried to fall.

She would not let him. She could feel more of those flows available to exploit, more things she could do . . . lots more. She squeezed another set of them together, less localized ones that seemed to be coming as much out of the floor as from anywhere. The man lifted into the air, dangling like a doll, like Aggie's clown doll the other day: as helpless, as easy to control. Aggie picked another spot—squeezed—

"Aggie, *no!*" It was Karen's voice, but Aggie wasn't paying much attention. She stood, eyes narrowed, watching Walsh twist and moan in the air, clutching his head, turning redder and redder in the face.

Karen's protesting voice meant very little in the face of that sound, which Aggie suddenly found intensely satisfying. He was suddenly all the kids who had ever taunted her in the playground, everyone who had ever followed her home from school and poked her with sticks like someone poking an animal through the bars of the cage; and here was her chance to get revenge for all those attacks, all those little indignities, all at once. . . .

She could see inside Walsh, now, the place in the brain which was most vulnerable to the kind of squeezing she was doing: a spot where a quick in-turn of the flows, like snapping your fingers, would put out the cruel mind underneath it like hitting the wall-switch for the light. The air buzzed louder around her as she made sure of the spot—

"No, Aggie!" Karen cried. "Don't kill him!"

"But he hurt *you*," Aggie said, grim. It astounded her, a little, that someone as young-seeming as Karen should have so quickly forgotten the law of the playground. An eye for an eye: he pushes you, you push him. He tries to kill you—

"Aggie," Karen shouted through the buzzing, "I taught you never to use your powers this way—if you do, we'll be as bad as *they* are. Aggie, *please!*"

Aggie looked at him, twisting in the unseen wind, as the buzzing grew and grew. Shortly, she knew, if she allowed it to get much louder, it would snuff out his mind regardless of her not having done anything about that one specific spot.

Still—Aggie thought about that. Walsh was near unconsciousness; his fear and the rage were now almost wiped out by the sheer weight of the pain lying on his mind. Through that pain, like white noise or static on the TV, Aggie could make out features and areas that she hadn't been able to see before.

She found spots where the fear had left a kind of residue, where it had been accustomed to collect: a sort of mental bathtub ring. The image of her mother scrubbing the tub, the other night, recurred. And Aggie thought, *If you looked at the flows that are holding that stuff there—and destroyed them. Or just shifted them, the way you would make water run down a different channel from a mud puddle, by digging it a new channel with a stick. Then rubbing out the old one—*

Almost before she could explain it to herself, it started to happen. Old patterns unknit themselves, began to flow into new ones. In the concrete parts of Walsh's brain, the physical parts which only crudely reflected what was going on in the flows, tissue twisted and shifted. Walsh screamed.

Aggie was dimly aware of her parents looking on in horror, but transfixed. *This had better work,* she thought, while the process finished itself. *I don't want them to get into trouble—*

It was over. She let him fall to the ground again, groaning. Karen, who was beginning to recover herself somewhat, looked at Walsh in fear.

"He's not dead," Aggie said, with some satisfaction. It was not as complete as killing him would have been, maybe . . . but she could feel the buzzing in the air dying down, and the straightforward sense of relief—though still tinged with fear—from Karen.

Walsh was on his hands and knees, now, somehow managing to stagger even in this position. "What's going on?" he moaned. "Who are you?"

Confidently, Aggie stepped forward and looked at him with the evaluating gaze of a child examining a new mud pie. "Aggie Travis. What's your name?"

"Terry. Terry Walsh."

Aggie's mother came up behind her, putting her hands on her daughter's shoulders, and looking at Walsh with astonishment . . . and disquiet. "Aggie," she said softly, "what have you done?"

"I . . ." Aggie shrugged a little: there were no real words for it. If she did a lot more work of this kind, she was going to have to find new words for the things that were happening. And to judge by what Karen had said, there were people who could help her with that. . . .

"I erased the bad parts," Aggie said.

She smiled at Karen . . . Karen had been the first person who ever looked at her as if she wasn't a problem, but this was something new. Karen was looking back at her as if she was the solution.

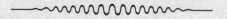

They all went out into the backyard briefly to get away into the fresh air; Aggie was grateful to escape the remnants of the buzzing inside the house.

"Others like Walsh will be here soon," Karen said sadly. If there was anything she wanted, it was to sit still, even if only for a few minutes, and accept the astonishment of what had just happened. "We've only bought a few minutes of freedom."

"Then you have to go," Aggie's mother said.

And now the heartbreak . . . there was no eluding it. "I have to take Aggie," Karen said.

Aggie's parents looked at Karen in utter shock. "You have to believe me," Karen said. "I'd do anything to change this. All I wanted was for Aggie to grow up with people who loved her. . . . Who understood what it was like."

Joe shook his head, put his arm around his daughter. "You're not taking her. She's our little girl. . . ."

Karen despaired, knowing that even now, the van would be looking for Walsh. She couldn't think what to do: too much had happened to her today.

But then, to her astonishment, Leslie made the choice. She took her husband by one arm. "You saw what happened, Joe!" she said. "That man came to take Aggie away!" She, too, reached out to Aggie . . . but the gesture was the light touch of someone who knows they will shortly have to let someone go. "Karen's right . . . she has to go."

Joe shook his head. "Then we'll take her. We'll hide her."

Karen shook her head sadly, knowing what kind of trail these people would leave behind them if they attempted it. It had been tried before, by very clever, very persistent people, but it had never worked, and once or twice it had almost given away all the other people involved in Sanctuary as well. "They'll find you," she said.

Karen knew Aggie could feel her certainty, as if from inside . . . and she found herself wondering what else this child might be able to do, given a few months' breathing space. "Karen's right!" Aggie said. "I need to be with people who are like me."

Joe held onto her. "I love you. I can't let you go. . . ."

"She wants to be safe," Leslie said, beginning to sniffle, but holding herself together by main force.

Joe looked at his wife, looked at Karen . . .

. . . then, finally, looked down at Aggie. "You're always going to be my little girl," he said, trying to hold in the tears, and failing. "Promise you'll come back someday soon."

Aggie was crying too, now, and so was Leslie. "I love you, Daddy," she said, and kissed him, and turned and kissed her mother.

They all turned and looked at Karen.

"I'll take good care of her," she said.

Though later, as Karen drove away with Aggie, and her hurriedly packed bag, and the clown doll, she wondered whether—shortly—it might not be the other way around. . . .

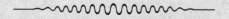

The wars of evolution are fought over generations, Karen thought, much later, out on the pouring dark of the Interstate, alone with the headlights and the stars, and a little girl sleeping in the back seat as they made their way toward Sanctuary. *But maybe the biggest changes come from the smaller battles, the ones that last just moments. Maybe, ten thousand years from now, a new race may look back and say, this was a turning point. . . .*

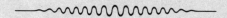

DIANE DUANE's first novel, The Door into Fire, *was published in 1979. Since then she has published more than twenty science fiction and fantasy novels, including a number of* Star Trek *novels that have become bestsellers. Duane has developed* Star Trek *stories in more media than any other author. In addition to novels, she writes extensively for the screen, including more than forty animation scripts for every major animation studio and the memorable episode "Where No One Has Gone Before" for* Star Trek: The Next Generation.

"A Feasibility Study" is one of the most famous 1960s Outer Limits
episodes, by the incomparable scriptwriter Joe Stefano. Here's the question Stefano posed: When a government or a large corporation wants to try something new, they begin with a feasibility study. What if aliens are taking the same tack?

A Feasibility Study

Adaptation by Michael Marano
Original screenplay by Joseph Stefano

Lightning, impossibly slow.

It tears night sky as a blade tears dark fabric; it widens in a shaft of harsh daylight, becoming a cone of noon erasing the stars in its radiance.

The light has weight. It punches the earth, making it shudder.

It acquires the earth and air.

The lightning contracts and pulls itself upward to darkness as a great wind comes across new pavements, across tended lawns and the badly made roofs of houses that rattle as atmosphere rushes to fill the vacuum created by the unnatural and sudden absence of dozens of houses and scores of souls.

Drawn into light, a community dies, leaving a deep scar upon the Earth where loose dirt shifts in small tumbles.

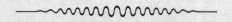

Ralph Cashman dreamt of falling.

He tumbled toward a dark countryside.

But this time the dream was different. Ralph fell at night. Ralph fell turning, among stars.

The ground rushed toward him.

The roar of the wind was at once the roar of his blood. It deafened him as he died upon impact—

—as he started, now awake, gripping sheets damp with his sweat.

His bedroom came into a soft and muted focus. His head ached, his mouth was dry: consequences of too much drink the night before. His throat was tight, his chest felt full of cotton wool: consequences of crying in his sleep.

The dream of falling to an inevitable, predestined death crept upon Ralph whenever he refused to face some dark fear while awake.

But why had he dreamed of stars?

The focus of his vision became sharper.

The ache in his head became sharper.

Turning in bed, Ralph reached over white and undulant sheets for his wife.

"Rhea?" he said softly.

As was true so often, she was not there.

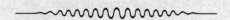

The sky was wrong.

Rhea Cashman stepped along the front walk of her home and found her gaze drawn upward, as if someone standing on a rise above her had made a gesture to get her attention. A fog, breathing and thin, with a hint of light about it—as if noon sun refracted through it—hung above the houses on her street, above the treetops, seeming to touch the odd chimney or TV aerial. It was a winter sky, come close to the earth. Looking into it, she felt as she had as a little girl on the day of the first snowfall. But the air was hot, moist, oppressive in its humidity—the air of deep summer, of a season several months past.

A mist, finer than the fog, finer than drizzle, filled the air. It did not fall, nor did it wet the sidewalk. Despite the fog, despite the mist, there was no dew on the shrubs or on the lawn. The air in her lungs felt dry as the heated air that filled her house when the furnace was going, on the coldest days.

Beyond the winter sky, visible behind the soft gray and the low fog in a manner that reminded Rhea of the ghost of a TV signal behind the snow of static, was another sky that made her think of the pictures in her mother's Bible illustrating the Book of Exodus. It was a sky of churning clouds . . . dark, with a hint of some powerful Will behind them.

The light of the sun was diffuse, too brightly white for so early in the day.

The tolling of church bells some blocks away brought Rhea out of her contemplation of the sky. The sound was muffled, as if the vibration struck against cotton-like walls of a sealed box.

She stepped down the walk, to get the Sunday paper, telling herself that she would not read the front page and *tisk!* to herself in consternated worry, that she would wait until she got inside and perhaps had breakfast with Ralph before she let world events get her in a tizzy . . . but she knew that as soon as she saw the paper, she would be unable to resist the small comfort that worry would afford her.

The paper was not there.

She checked the usual places their paperboy tossed the paper, thinking to herself how much the boy . . . and all the other kids in this neighborhood over the age of twelve . . . unnerved her. The paper-boy seemed *incomplete,* sullen and self-absorbed. Something was missing from the adolescents born right after the war. Some profound absence she could not articulate, manifest in so small a thing as not bothering to place a paper near a doorstep.

The church bells faded as she searched; they would ring again as the top of the hour neared.

And another sound asserted itself.

Like a congregation of birds, faint, yet omni-present as the chirping of crickets in the night, with a metallic tinge. The sound pressed upon her mind, like the whisper of someone standing too close to her ear, or the beat of an insect's wings against her face.

Rhea looked about, trying to fathom where the sound came from. As she strained to hear, a new thought made her chest tighten with anxiety. She indulged the small worry, and went toward her house, fretting that stepping outside might have been a fatal error of judgment.

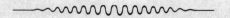

Ralph stood behind the living room bar, his head somewhat cleared after his shower and shave, his state of mind somewhat restored upon putting on a fresh suit.

Hair of the dog, he thought, as he filled a shot glass.

He had spent yesterday at the country club of a full partner in his firm, playing a friendly game of golf. In the friendly interests of his professional advancement, Ralph had lost. The partner had taken a shine to Ralph because he had a reputation for "knowing when the guy sitting across the table's mouth was dry." The partner had spoken of certain factors that his fellows on the board looked for in the promotion of sharp-eyed executives. One such factor was "corporate spunk," a "go get 'em" attitude that "gets things done."

Hence, Ralph spending last night before the television, unwinding with a bottle, recovering from the day.

Hence, the bad dreams.

Hence, Ralph donning a suit this morning.

Hence, Ralph going in to the office today, to get a head start on an upcoming fiscal report, to show some of that "go get 'em" spirit that will get him the attention that will get him a promotion that will force him to work harder all the time.

Hair of the dog.

The shot glass trembled in his hand.

The front door slammed.

The sound cut through his head, made his ears ring.

Rhea walked toward the bar, frowning.

"So, what's this morning's catastrophe?" he asked, not meaning to sound grumpy. He kept his eye on the glass, trying to steady it before tossing back its contents. Rhea positioned herself at the bar, taking his full attention away from his folk remedy for his self-inflicted malady.

"Ralph?" she asked, taking a pretzel from an oversized brandy snifter they kept on the bar—a function it had been conscripted to upon their receiving it as an anniversary gift last year. "Is fallout anything like rain?"

Ralph looked up from his shot. Rhea's face was etched with worry, a look she bore at times even in her sleep. The worry would seem incongruous on the face of any woman except Rhea as she leaned against the bar, munching a pretzel with the posture of a teenage girl pondering a dreamy boy.

Is fallout anything like rain?

That was good. Even for Rhea, who'd worried a few months ago that the colony of ants that had gotten into their medicine cabinet would become, somehow, by ingesting the vitamins there, impervious to DDT.

Ralph turned his back to her, unable to bear the look of disdain that would cross her face as he downed his drink. He suspected that he was a bit in the doghouse already, having spent the night drinking, not singing, with Mitch Miller (and not sitting quietly with her, the way they used to spend Saturday nights before they moved out of the city, before they had ever thought of owning a TV).

He downed the shot, fire running along his raw throat to his gut as he convinced himself that the booze was taking the edge off of his "morning after."

He turned back to Rhea, trying to smile.

"It's raining?" he asked, his voice a bit harsh.

Frowning, Rhea brought the pretzel to her mouth, in the way she would bring her thumb up to bite the nail. She still leaned against the bar like a bobby soxer on the counter of a soda fountain.

"No, It's not raining. But it's doing *some*thing, and I'll bet it's radioactive."

She bit the pretzel.

"There's an uncanny noise, too."

Ralph started to laugh, but laughing hurt his head. Things Rhea deemed "uncanny" were usually just a little odd. He flashed her a grin, instead.

"No wonder you're so insecure," he said. "Eating pretzels for breakfast."

He took the pretzel from her hand and took a bite. *Now or never,* he thought.

He came from behind the bar, and walked toward the foyer. "I'm going to the office."

He felt her gaze on his back, heard her quick steps to catch up to him.

"Ralph! You haven't even had any breakfast!" The tiny urgency in her voice awoke a small guilt that he'd convinced himself he would not feel.

He raised the pretzel and smiled at her.

"I'm having a pretzel."

"Really, Ralph! Do you have to give in to this thing on Sundays, too?"

Ralph fished his keys off the table in the foyer.

"What thing?"

"This success compulsion that's making us all widows! Really, Ralph. . . ."

"I wish you'd stop saying 'Really, Ralph!' It sounds like you're calling me 'mealy mouthed.'"

Rhea dropped her shoulders; her worried look faded.

"Come have a normal breakfast, at least."

She kissed him, and walked toward the kitchen, muttering a soft, "*Really, Ralph!*" as she did so.

Ralph finished his pretzel and opened the front door.

Outside intruded.

Ralph attributed his unease, his vertigo upon opening the door, to his hangover. But it was much more of a fundamental shifting of normality than that.

Outside intruded.

The street, the trees, the grass, and the pavement all pressed upon his senses, as if the very quality of light were made more sublime. The street looked as it did after the eye doctor had given Ralph pupil-dilating drops. But all his senses felt overwhelmed, including his sense of balance, which was now giving him the uneasy feeling of having just stepped off a roller coaster.

The air felt like high summer, though now it was fall. The heat, the heavy and terrible heat, was hazy, oily, impossibly *still*, not at all the heat of an Indian summer. There was no sun in the sky. The clouds seemed lit by a diffused light, as if a great sun filled the sky behind the layered clouds from directly above, and not slanting in from the east.

'Earthquake weather.'

Ralph had heard the phrase during his first trip to California. Still and heavy air (only half as still and heavy as this) had blanketed the city, making everyone nervous, edgy. This morning *felt* like California, too. Ralph, who had always lived on the eastern seaboard, had been in a state of perpetual disorientation, unable to find his bearings in an absurd place where the sun set over the sea.

He pulled the door shut and stepped off the modest porch to his front walk.

Falling . . .

As Ralph placed his foot on the walk, for just an instant, he had the same sense of falling as he had had in the dream. A cold sweaty chill spread across his back.

He headed toward his car at the curb, pulling at his shirt collar, which was already softening in the damp heat. The faint smell of dry cleaning fluid rose from his suit.

He was dimly aware of a sound, a whine like the metallic chirping of birds, when a movement in the driveway next door caught his eye. He gave the sound no more notice than he would the ambient rumble of the furnace in winter time.

His next-door neighbor, Dr. Holm, stood in his driveway, staring at his car. This was the first time in a long time that Ralph had seen one of his neighbors standing still.

Ralph hadn't really had the chance to chat with
the doctor since he and his wife (*Oh, what was his
wife's name, again? Alice? No. Andrea!*) had moved in.

He walked across the lawn.

"Good morning, Doctor."

Dr. Holm looked up from his car with a slight
and pleasant neighbor-smile.

"Good morning, Mr. Cashman."

"Care to diagnose this weather?"

Dr. Holm glanced up at the churning sky, main-
taining his half-smile, though now with a grim look
in his eyes.

He shook his head, in a single gesture answering
Ralph's question and commenting upon the weather.

"*And,*" he said, adding to his non-verbal com-
ment, "there's something wrong with my car."

Ralph sized up the car. It was this year's model.

"Maybe you're out of gas?"

"No."

Ralph leaned on the front of the chassis, the posture men must take before they open the hood of a
car. Doctors like Holm didn't go in much for grease-
monkey work. A deep cut on their hands, and they
wouldn't be able to practice. He was about to suggest fetching Rhea, so she and Ralph could get
under the hood and so use fixing Holm's car as an
icebreaker to invite Holm and (*Andrea? yes*) Andrea
over for. . . .

The front door to the Holm house opened.

And Andrea Holm stood in the doorway.

She looked lovely.

Something about her seemed different, a kind of melancholy prettiness. She had an air about her like some ancient saint cast in stone or plaster.

Before Ralph could take a breath to greet her, he realized that she simply did not see him.

"Simon?"

Her voice held deep sorrow. Ralph, upon hearing it, wished he were invisible, not merely unseen.

Holm turned away from Ralph, moving with desperate urgency.

His shoulders were thrown back in the posture of expectation Ralph saw in young men being called in for a promotion.

Andrea Holm seemed to collect herself. "We didn't say good-bye."

Dr. Holm's shoulders dropped.

"I'll be gone when you get back."

Holm nodded slightly. Without seeing Holm's face, Ralph saw how much that that nod spoke.

She closed the door gently, as one would close the door of a sick room. Mrs. Holm had been wearing the sort of clothes that Rhea's fashion magazines touted as "perfect for travel": outfits based on the smart suits the former First Lady, now First Widow, had worn while disembarking from Air Force One.

Holm turned.

Ralph spoke too loudly and too helpfully.

"Look," Ralph said. "I'm going downtown. I'll drop you."

Holm was still for the span of a heartbeat, then responded.

"Thank you, Mr. Cashman. I'm going to church."

Ralph and Dr. Holm had gotten into the car and settled in their seats when Ralph heard Rhea call from the doorway of his house: "Ralph! Ralph, come and eat!"

He held a moment, key in the ignition. Dr. Holm seemed uneasy, perhaps afraid that he and Ralph would be delayed just long enough for Mrs. Holm to emerge from their house again.

Rhea walked nervously toward the car, taking a moment to look up and glare at the weather, her fear of fallout forgotten for a moment. Ralph opened his window. She had on one of her patented scolding looks; maybe she'd insist he sit in the car as she ran into the house to bring out a scrambled egg sandwich. But then she glanced at Dr. Holm in the passenger seat, and whatever unfancy thing she'd intended to say was forgotten as she smoothed her humidity-dampened hair and smiled.

"Good morning, doctor," she said as she reached Ralph's door.

"Good morning, Mrs. Cashman."

Rhea had placed her hand on the door, by the rearview mirror. Ralph placed his on top of hers; it felt cool in the ugly heat.

"The doctor's car won't start. Go take a look under the hood, Rhea."

Ralph turned to the doctor.

"She's one of those housewives who can fix *any*-thing!"

In trying to reassure Dr. Holm about his car, Ralph realized that he had perhaps reminded his neighbor of the failing of his own marriage. Ralph's shoulders tightened; a flash of headache pinched his brow.

Dr. Holm responded with a slight nod and a polite smile.

Rhea had not noticed Ralph's quick unease, and was smiling prettily at Ralph's compliment.

Still smiling, blushing slightly behind the flush the weather had brought to her face, she said softly, "Really, Ralph. . . ."

Ralph wanted so badly to kiss her, but dared not, for fear of embarrassing the doctor.

"Go take a look." He caught himself about to say "*sweetheart.*" He withdrew his hand from Rhea's, started the ignition. "And get out of this . . . *rain,* or whatever it is."

"I'll see you later," she said, and Ralph found himself wanting to kiss her again.

He pulled away from the curb.

The mist became thicker toward the end of the block, becoming a bank like that which would drift off a river at night.

Ralph rode the brake as he drove.

Traveling through the fog was like falling through grim and heavy clouds.

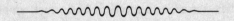

Rhea was tempted.

She loved putting things right, making things work. She wished she could fix the vague and shadowy things that made her worry as expeditiously as she could fix machines.

She walked to Dr. Holm's car, thinking of her girlhood heroine—Nancy Drew's friend George, who could fix anything, especially cars, and who never waited for men to get off their duffs and get things done.

Smiling, Rhea opened the hood of Dr. Holm's car.

The engine compartment was empty.

The thick smell of oil wafted from the empty compartment. Rhea, as she tasted the bite of the oil, realized she'd been staring at the compartment with her mouth open.

The heat, the wet air, the stink of the oil, the nastiness of Ralph's little prank, and the fact that he had cajoled Dr. Holm (*of all people!*) to participate in the prank, all made her shoulders clench. A knot collected at the back of her neck as she turned to look at the taillights of Ralph's car, which were muted and dimmed by the fog.

She almost growled.

"Really, Ralph!"

A movement of air.

A displacement of space.

A sudden heaviness, and the creak of the car's chassis. The sensation of the open hood jumping against her upraised hands.

Rhea started, as if someone had snuck up on her.

She looked down as her arms—without her volition—were about to slam the hood down.

The engine was *there.*

Simply *there,* as if it had come into existence in the second she'd had her head turned away. The hard edges of the motor block, the fan casing, the battery, for just the merest of instants, seemed smooth—without enough definition to accommodate sharpness and angularity.

Rhea stared at the motor, too stunned to react.

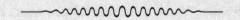

"We're neighbors, but we're not really friends."

No, thought Ralph. *No, that won't do.*

Ralph hunched over the wheel, squinting through the windshield at the meager crescent of visibility made by the sweep of the wipers.

The fog rolled over the hood of his car, tumbling, like clouds. Ralph thought uneasily of turning stars, and wondered why he should think of such an absurd thing. The weather—the hot wetness of *everything*—seemed to affect the brakes. At each corner, the shocks bounced, as if the distribution of the car's weight were different. Most likely the brake pads couldn't create enough friction because of the oily dampness.

"We've been neighbors, but never really been friends."

No, thought Ralph. *That wouldn't do it, either.*

Dr. Holm sat beside Ralph, lost in private contemplation of some angry sorrow. Ralph could feel . . . the *grief* (there was no other word for it) . . . radiating off the man.

He took a breath.

"We've been next-door neighbors for over a year now, but we're not next-door friends, yet."

That was good, thought Ralph. *That was a good way to put it.*

Dr. Holm, as if roused from a light nap, shook his head slightly and looked at Ralph.

"Excuse me?" he said softly.

"Never mind. . . ." Ralph swallowed. "Only, I wish we were friends so I could ask you what's breaking you up."

Holm frowned, just detectably, in surprise.

Ralph realized what he'd just said.

"How did you know my wife and I were separating?"

"I didn't!" Trying not to sound defensive, Ralph softened his tone. "I meant, you know, '*breaking you up inside.*' Just an . . . just an expression."

Silence, a moment.

Holm stared ahead, through the windshield, as Ralph strained to see through the mist that hung low over the road. Traffic was light—surprisingly light— even for a Sunday as foul and fair as this.

"Gee," said Ralph. "And you've only been married how long?"

Holm spoke as if listing a catalogue of blithely committed wrongs.

"A year and a week and . . . long enough to see that it was an honest mistake."

"They're the worst kind."

Holm said nothing. The car kept rocking and swaying, oddly.

Ralph said, "You want to talk about it?"

"No," Holm said very softly.

Then, as if the desire to not 'want to talk about it' were eclipsed by the *necessity* to talk about it, Holm blurted, "She's what the magazine writers are calling the 'spiritually awakened woman.'"

"Whatever that means."

Holm looked out at the gray silhouettes of trees going past the misted windows.

"She was a writer. Newspapers. She wrote 'think pieces' that really did make people think."

More gray and featureless suburban landscape went past. The greens of well-tended lawns seemed drained of vibrancy, as they do just before the coming of a sudden summer storm.

"Now she thinks our marriage is the beginning of her 'mental and spiritual deterioration.' Those are her words."

Church bells signaling the start of ten o'clock mass tolled up the street. Ralph could not see the church up the road, nor could he gauge the distance from the church by the sound of the bells. They seemed muffled, somehow.

Ralph said, "My father, rest in peace, he used to say 'Ralphie, marry a dumb girl or a smart girl, but keep away from the intelligent ones."

Ralph smiled.

And was pleased to see Dr. Holm smile as well.

He peered ahead through the clouded windshield.

"That your church?" he asked.

Holm palm-rubbed his window, peered out, nodded.

Ralph pulled to the curb, felt the car rock in a way that made him wonder if he should have the attendant at the gas station downtown give the brakes a look.

Holm opened the door, put one leg outside the car.

"Thank you for the lift, Mr. Cashman."

"'Ralph,' now that we know each other."

Holm half-smiled, got out, and spoke another "Thank you" as he closed the door and waved. The slam made the car creak and groan and rock.

Ralph ignored the annoyance, smiled, and waved at Dr. Holm as he pulled away from the curb.

Ralph, out of habit, glanced at his rearview mirror. Holm in his dark suit was a single mark of solidity in the misted air, alone in the open expanse of asphalt before his church. Soon, mist on the rear window made Holm invisible as he stepped toward the church.

Ralph turned his gaze back to the windshield.

The church bells fell quiet as he rounded the corner.

"Go get 'em."

The fog thickened as he drove. The small clusters of mist seemed like movement in the corner of his sight as they imposed themselves, one on top of the other, within the smeary crescent made by the path of the wipers. The houses on either side of the street before him faded to outlines in the haze; green lawns were now almost colorless.

The sound that he'd half-heard before as he was stepping out of his house came again into his awareness— shrill and sibilant over the drone of the car engine.

Something *stirred* inside him—a drowsy paralysis akin to what he felt at times when he stared at the TV late at night. He couldn't let go of his irritation at the driving conditions, nor could he consciously indulge it.

Ralph turned on the car radio.

The sound.

It struck him, loud, flooding out of the car speakers like a moving wall. His ears rang. His teeth pulled together painfully. His every muscle clenched. Yet he felt a sickening complacence, an urge to tolerate the wall of sibilant noise.

He winced.

Shut off the radio.

Then leaned hard on the brakes as another wall loomed before him, a wall of storm clouds piled in churning layers, hanging close to the road like the gray hem of a giant's robe.

Falling . . .

Ralph pitched forward as the car rocked and tipped with the force of the sudden stop. For an instant, he felt he was tumbling earthward through clouds.

The houses on either side of the road were invisible. The street seemed to simply *end* on the other side of the bank, as if Ralph could drive through the fog and plummet off a cliff.

Ralph waited a moment.

Let his heart slow.

He couldn't shake the sense of falling; feeling wrongly positioned in relation to the sun gave him tumbling vertigo for the span of a breath. It was *morning*, damnit. In the *autumn*. He was driving *east*. But the diffuse white light of the sun seemed to emanate from *behind* him.

He thought of going back, to Rhea. To a morning of reading the paper and drinking coffee and an afternoon of lovemaking and a nice dinner in town. She deserved that. *He* deserved that.

"Go get 'em."

Ralph took a deep breath, rolled down the car window and leaned his head out.

The sound pressed on his senses. Made an itch in his ears at once like an extremity gone to sleep and like rising in an elevator through a skyscraper. His hangover, perhaps, making him oversensitive? The buzz of high tension wires?

The moist heat pressed itself like a caul upon his face.

The bank of fog hung unmoving in the air, unfocused like the corners of a dim room.

He'd try to drive through. If the fog proved too thick, he'd go back to Rhea. He'd nap away the hangover and treat her right—like a queen—for the rest of the day. "*Go get 'em*" was only a good idea as far as one could "*go*" safely.

Ralph pulled his head in, rolled up the window and drove forward.

Into fog and its gray night.

He could see almost nothing beyond the hood of his car, only the vague suggestion of a road ahead and below.

His car heaved as if he drove on slick, uneven gravel. He lost traction after a few yards; did the fog hide an oil slick? The suspension pitched. The sound of the tires on pavement became muted, wet.

Ralph stopped the car slowly, not wanting to lock into a skid on a road he could not see.

Hell with this, he thought.

He opened the window again, to look the way he'd come as he backed out of the fog, not wanting to rely on the misted-over rear window.

Fingers of fog slithered into the car with the speed of water.

The fog itched.

The fog burned.

Became a fur of irritation in his lungs.

Ralph coughed, brought his breast pocket handkerchief to his mouth.

The sound, the whine, vibrated in his joints.

He wanted to throw the car in reverse and careen back through the haze to the street he knew. But he could wreck the car, losing his way off the road and piling onto a lawn or into a house.

He opened the car door, handkerchief still over his face, to see if he could pilot the car by looking down to the curbside, holding his breath if he had to. . . .

Movement.

Shifting.

The car rocking.

Quickly, violently . . .

A wet noise.

Something struck the windshield, as if the car had hit a bird in mid-flight.

Ralph looked up.

And saw a hand pressed against the windshield, saw *into* the hand, saw tendons, layers of scabbed flesh, arthritic joints, metallic protrusions like lumps of solderant, ruined skin crying lymph.

The hand left a smear across the glass as it pulled away, upward.

Ralph tumbled out of the car.

Falling . . . out of the sane world of his car to one where weight shifted and centers of gravity were misaligned.

And struck an uneven surface like a hardened mass of fat, a surface holding a hidden light, glowing, alloyed with metal that shone with the shifting luminosity of tinsel and brass.

His hands, his clothes were dusted with fine metal filings as they came into contact with the surface.

He looked up, to the roof of his car.

Did not see what must have been on the roof that placed its hand upon the windshield.

The fog in his lungs itched.

He pulled himself up by the car door. Ready to drive, consequences be damned, back the way he came.

Out of the brooding fog . . .

Out of the grayness . . .

Inarticulate shadows took solidity.

Shapeless.

Lumbering with a perverted grace.

Three parodies of the human form came toward him.

Monks of wax, melted, shambling, as if toward vespers, in hoodless robes through which corrupted flesh seeped in patches as blood and yellow suppuration seep through thin bandages. Eruptions of cyst-smooth metal on their swollen faces, hands, and arms. Skin the texture of dried river mud, glistening, as if dusted with an irritating glitter set with impossible precision in each pore.

Closer . . .

Blotches of skin with shards of metal growing in patterns like those of whiskers on a man's face.

Ralph turned from the car and ran.

And saw the robed thing behind him just briefly as it brought its hand over his face.

Warm, clear secretions of ravaged flesh ran down in tears from his brow.

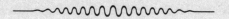

Simon Holm felt no comfort this day in the house of God as he dipped his fingers in the bénitier by the church door and inscribed a cross in cool holy water down from his forehead and across his breast.

The water, in the moist heat, did not dry upon his forehead, but warmed, sweat-like, upon his brow.

Once, the act of crossing a church threshold had given him peace. Even during the worst times of his internship, when he had worked days at a stretch in an ill-lit emergency room surrounded by human suffering, Simon had still felt a healing in his heart when he retreated to the hospital chapel. In this way he confronted the horror of existence.

But now, in his troubled heart, there was no horror to face.

Now there was absence.

How to confront a non-thing? How to dignify the soul while confronted with emptiness?

Simon found what peace he could in melancholy withdrawal.

The church was empty, more so than usual, as Simon kneeled, crossed himself again, and took a pew near the center of the church.

Father Fontanna was a lonely white-haired figure at the pulpit, dim in the muted light filtering from the stained glass windows. The light did not strike the pulpit as it usually did, was not strong enough to illuminate the colored glass.

Father Fontanna spoke about the new encyclicals from Rome. After a few moments, Simon could not keep listening.

He wished to, but he could not break out of his brooding regret.

"*Andrea*" . . . from the Greek, "woman of strength." He had such passion for her strength, for her determination and focus. But now her strength called her away from his passion.

The first time he had seen her, she had been crying.

And working.

Simon had been finishing his pediatrics residency in a hospital just outside Chicago, where Catholic Charities had set up a ward to treat thalidomide children flown into the U.S.

His previous residency in orthopedics had left him unprepared.

Here, a hand extended from a child's shoulder without the intermediacy of upper arm or wrist.

Here, feet were joined to hips.

Here, fingers grew like buds from the rounded edge of incomplete elbows.

A drug, written as a prescription to soothe, had rewritten the bodies of these children in the womb.

Simon, on his way to the ward one evening, had seen Andrea seated on a couch near the nurse's station, quietly writing on a steno pad, quietly wiping away steady tears with a tissue, never turning her attention from the paper before her.

He learned, once on shift, that Andrea had come to write a piece on thalidomide children for the *Tribune*.

At his next break, he found her in the cafeteria, looking lovely and clear-eyed, like a woman who had not cried, going over her copy with a blue pencil. Longing to know her, longing to know her passion and caring, he ventured the offer of a cup of wretched hospital coffee.

And months later, longing to be with her, longing to share his life with her, he ventured the offer of a ring.

What that ring now meant, upon the hand of a woman now riding in the back of a taxi out of his life, he could not fathom.

Without thought, without purpose, Simon rose with the rest of this day's meager congregation to take communion.

The oppressive heat and mugginess made the blood of Christ bitter as vinegar on his lips, made the flesh of Christ wilted and stale on his tongue.

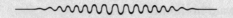

Ground glass, in his lungs.

"Rhea . . ."

Ralph Cashman, on his hands and knees, reached out into empty fog.

"Rhea . . ."

His heart beating blood that felt too thick in his veins, he crawled over a landscape of soil that glowed with the light of mica, yet was as hard and unyielding as dull steel. The fog was a carpet upon the ground, parting in wisps as he heaved his way forward in a place where the sanity of weight and centers of gravity were warped.

The skin on his face and hands itched. The backs of his hands were covered with glimmering flecks like those in sunlit granite. He could not scrape them off no matter how hard he tried.

A pulling sensation on his face, where a new and unwelcome weight of deformity grew in patches.

Beneath his skin, the sensation of a sunburn.

Every joint in his body felt sprained.

A whining hum filled his ears. He wanted to stop and surrender to hopelessness. The hum vibrated in his breast, pressed upon his ears, meshed with the sound of rushing blood and the sound of rushing air—the sounds of falling.

Ralph Cashman crawled through a white and undulant mass of cloud that seemed about to open and let him drop to the distant earth.

He crawled away from things not of the earth he knew.

Toward his home.

Toward his wife.
He reached forward.
"Rhea . . ."
As was true so often, she was not there.

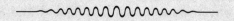

Simon was tired.

The muggy heat, the heavy air, the sadness he carried, all drained his energy.

A high-pitched whine echoed on the street, making him feel as if he had a headache without the pain.

He thought of going to the hospital, making Sunday rounds, consulting in the emergency room. What he *should* do was return to his office in the basement of the house and dictate his patients' records for the hospital typing pool. But he could not bear having only his own voice for company, replayed over and over again on the Dictaphone.

No, best to have a shower and a fresh change of clothes. Best to go to the hospital and have something of this day besides a new emptiness.

He'd made better time walking home from church than he had by accepting Mr. Cashman's slow and careful ride through the fog. Church was five blocks away. How had he gotten into the habit of driving every day, for every*thing?*

The Church of the Immaculate Conception was an anomaly: an old parish church, now surrounded by prefabricated, flimsy houses erected in the postwar building frenzy. What was once a remote church that people walked miles along country roads to reach, he now drove five blocks to attend.

Simon glanced at the unstarting new car in the driveway.

Pulled out his keys and unlocked the door—a thing which seemed absurd, as he and Andrea had moved here "to be safe." Yet there was an air of thuggery here among the young—the children of privilege and comfort—that he could not fathom; at times, he wasn't certain if the threat were real, but it *felt* real.

He climbed the stairs to the bedroom.

And there saw Andrea, sitting on the edge of the bed with the telephone against her ear. In the ill-defined light, she seemed a day-lit shadow, solid in the darkness of her outline.

Her face, surrounded by a hazy corona, held a look of regret.

In mid-step, in mid-thought, Simon glanced downward, saw Andrea's packed bags.

He looked up at her; she had decided to stay with him, to stay with their marriage.

He was about to speak when Andrea shifted on the edge of the bed, bringing herself by that small movement into materiality, out of her day-lit shadow.

She looked at him.

"No . . ." she said, shaking her head.

She replaced the receiver.

"I just haven't been able to get a taxi. The phone is out of order."

Andrea turned her head away, as if to ponder the phone.

Simon went to her, not knowing why.

With no other course of action before him, he picked up the phone and dialed the operator. Andrea slipped away from him, picked up her travel case from the bureau in the corner to set it with her suitcases on the floor.

A nothing-cry came from the telephone receiver, like the song of distant, sad, mechanical birds. The sound pressed itself into his awareness, intrusive as an alien thought. The tightness in his chest made him resign this one small effort to facilitate his wife's leaving him, to expedite the pain of having to say goodbye yet again.

He replaced the receiver.

Andrea looked at him and smiled softly, sadly.

"Didn't you believe me?"

Simon wished to speak, to answer her with something meaningful, something that would exonerate him from all the questions he had not answered, all the pleas, the requests, the accusations.

He stepped behind her and placed his hands on her shoulders. He spoke independently of his will, articulating the ache in his heart.

"Don't go, Andrea."

She crossed her arms before her, and gently removed his hands with a firm, sad kindness that hurt in a way that a gesture of anger never could.

She turned to him.

"How would you do it, Simon?"

She dropped her shoulders, smoothed her jacket.

"Wouldn't it hurt you, or make you very old or very resentful? How would you adjust to such an immoral relationship?"

Andrea, using her profound skill with words to articulate that which cannot be articulated without abstraction, that which cannot be articulated without the need to ponder its implication. How she spoke was how she wrote: '*think pieces*' pronounced and applied to their private life.

"Immoral?"

"Living with someone you don't love. Loving with someone you don't . . . love?"

"We're married."

"Marriage is no substitute for love, Simon."

She stepped around him, toward the neatly made bed.

"But *I* haven't stopped loving you!" His voice was more desperate than he'd intended. She turned, fixing him with her deep and lovely eyes.

"I'm disappointed," he said. "And I'm angry. And maybe just a little frightened. But I still love you."

"No," she said. "Not if you won't bend, just a little. Not if you can't let me have some part of my life to live my own way."

He stepped to the bed, sat, then fumbled for his cigarettes and lighter on the night stand.

She stepped close to him as he lit.

"Love isn't supposed to weaken, Simon, but it should make you able to understand another person's heartbeat, even if the rhythm is different from yours."

Simon watched wisps of smoke rise from his cigarette, almost invisible in the harsh white light that came in from the window.

Andrea said, "I can't live with you if life has to be lived according to your prescriptions. I can't! No matter how benevolent or secure you make it, it's slavery."

Simon looked at her, at the pain in her eyes, the anger and the hurt.

"It's a *kind of slavery!*" she said.

And Simon wondered how she could say those words so steadfastly.

Sanity.

A rough edge of asphalt, like a jagged step.

Ralph Cashman pulled himself onto an earthly street of concrete, like a drowning man pulling himself on to a raft.

Coughing, still in fog.

He stood, tried to walk.

Stumbled.

Crawled again.

Until he emerged from the bank of fog that had held him prisoner to a street that in another existence, he would have known to be near his home, as much as "home" could have meaning, now.

In the brighter light, out of the dense fog, he saw beads of silver affixed to his hands like dew upon a stem.

Still crawling, on an empty street, Ralph Cashman sobbed.

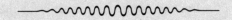

Andrea Holm's car keys sat on the hall table next to an elegant candy dish that she had never bothered to fill.

Looking up from the table, she glanced through the hall window. From across the lawn she saw Rhea Cashman, screwdriver in hand, puttering with a window-mounted air conditioner. She had a look upon her face like a schoolgirl intent upon a difficult lesson.

Andrea envied her sense of security, her sense of place and competence. Often, Andrea had seen Mrs. Cashman puttering around the house: replacing the valve on the garden hose faucet; looking under the hood of her car while her husband, with smiling confidence, turned the ignition at her direction; replacing the wiring of the front doorbell of her home.

Her husband allowed her to *have* ability, allowed her to function in the milieu of "wife" without restricting her gift to fix and putter and repair. Simon could not have a wife with the ability to write, or care, or sacrifice. Andrea had lived, in the past year, within a home—and a marriage—made into a trap by virtue of their convenience.

Suddenly, Mrs. Cashman looked up.

Startled, she dropped her screwdriver, giving Andrea a falsely sheepish smile. She pulled the window frame down on the air conditioner, setting it fast. Andrea heard the unit start with a rumble as Mrs. Cashman walked away from the window.

The unit had not been broken.

Mrs. Cashman was puttering with it for the sake of puttering, perhaps tightening the screws that held a metal plate in place.

Andrea had seen this agitation before, this nervous fixing of things that did not need fixing.

She'd done a story on brushfires in an impossibly dry summer. Waiting for disaster to come, the firemen she interviewed had checked and rechecked their equipment, replaced spark plugs on vehicles that had been replaced the day before.

Floorboards creaked above her.

Simon was pacing.

Andrea went to the door, intent upon leaving. If she faced Simon again, she'd inflict more hurt upon both of them.

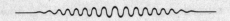

A face in a window.

Curtains shut quickly.

Ralph cried out in a voice not much louder than a whisper.

Hoarse and guttural.

Trying to warn.

Trying to explain.

Crawling, he ran his spangled hand over grass that was the wrong color green under this foreign sky.

He stood.

Forced his way forward.

Toward Rhea.

Toward his wife.

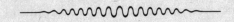

"Andrea! Wait!"

Simon's voice was rich with an anguish he did not wish to reveal.

Anguish which caused Andrea to stop.

And which shamed him in a way he could not articulate.

He stood in the doorway of his home.

Andrea, sitting in the car at the edge of the driveway, shifted into park. She looked over her shoulder at him, through the fog-misted car window, with a calmly hurt expression on her face. The engine made a counterpoint to the silence between them.

In willful contrast to the dash he'd just made down the stairs from the second floor, he slowly walked toward the car as Andrea rolled down the window.

In willful contrast to his plaintive cry, he spoke softly.

"This morning, I couldn't get it to start."

A sorry imitation of normalcy.

It shamed him in a way he could not articulate.

Andrea matched his falsely even tone.

"It must have been cold." An absurd thing to say, in the midst of this stifling heat. "It's all right now."

A pause.

"Andrea. . . ." He reached through the car window and shut off the ignition. "I want a wife who makes a house something to come home to. I'm not trying to deprive you of your rights. I don't want you running around the world with your camera and typewriter worrying about everyone else, when I need you here at home, with some of that Crusader instinct working for our marriage."

Simon leaned against the car, quickly looked over the expanse of their neatly plotted street.

"If marriage has become insignificant in this big troubled world of ours, maybe that's one of the reasons why the world has such big troubles!"

He looked back at Andrea.

"Simon . . ."

Her composure dissolved. Her voice cracked.

"Something bad is happening to my mind. At night, I lie beside you, and my mind keeps me awake. It cries. My mind cries."

She made her hands into fists and brought them to her face.

Simon reached in through the car window, gently brought her fists away.

Her hands opened in his, and he held them tightly. They were cool in the oppressive air.

"I lie there," she said. "And I go over my day, and I think, 'Is this all there is to it? Just the monotony, just the little labors that don't even exhaust my body, let alone my mind?' I'm suffocating, Simon. I thought marrying you would be the greatest adventure I'd ever know. But it isn't. It's a dead-end world walled in by curtains that don't even get dirty."

She pulled her hands away.

"Why must that be, Simon? I *want* to worry. I *want* to care about making this world a better place. Why is that wrong now, just because I'm married?"

"It isn't wrong! But I work *here,* in one place, one hospital. . . ."

"Twenty hours a day!"

"Then I want the other four with you! I don't want you running errands for some newspaper. Let them send someone who has the time. . . ."

With defeated quiet she said, "All I have is time."

Simon said softly, "When we have a child. . . ."

"I don't want to just *have* a child! I want to plan for it! I want to be ready for it! I want to at least *try* to better the world I'm going to bring it into!"

Simon drew a careful breath to speak careful words . . .

. . . when a woman's scream cut through the Sunday morning quiet.

His glance shot upward. Over the roof of the car he saw Rhea Cashman in the doorway of her home, her mouth wide open, her eyes bright with a look Simon recognized as the unaccepting shock of people who have rushed to the hospital to see critically injured loved ones, only to find that they have already died.

He followed her gaze.

Ralph Cashman stumbled up the walk.

Industrial accident.

The words flashed upon his mind, trying to impose some known debasement of human flesh on what had happened to his neighbor, trying to account for the shining protrusions leaking bloodless lymph on his face and hands as perhaps only imbedded shrapnel from a blast could. The swelling. The sparse coating of toxic-looking iridescence over his clothing. Simon thought, absurdly, of the scales of a bluefish.

But the protrusions.

The swelling.

The iridescence.

All were distributed evenly over Ralph's body— not focused on one side of him, as they would be on the victim of a concussive blast.

Ralph Cashman's face reminded Simon of a crash patient who had slipped out of unconsciousness only long enough to realize that he had lost a limb.

Simon recovered himself.

Ran to Mr. Cashman as he heard Andrea get out of the car behind him.

Mr. Cashman stumbled like a dying man.

Simon was about to grab hold of him when he saw that his neighbor's clothing smoked slightly.

The man collapsed to the walkway of red brick, metal-splotched hands covering his ruined face.

Simon bent down.

Reached for the stricken man.

A tortured whisper: *"Don't . . . touch . . . me! . . ."*

He rolled away from Simon's outstretched hand against the low hedges of the walk, exposing his face.

The protrusions were not embedded in his flesh.

They were eruptions, a corona of necrotic tissue at the root of each.

Simon looked up, saw that Andrea had gone to Mrs. Cashman, that she was holding her back from going to her husband.

He yelled to his wife.

"Call the hospital!!"

Simon looked down at his neighbor, wondering how to begin to treat such injuries.

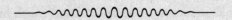

Andrea stumbled through the Cashman's doorway.

In the foyer, she looked for the phone, hearing Rhea's voice behind her, talking in panicked tones to Simon.

Andrea saw the phone.

When she grabbed the receiver, a thousand voices, fluting and high pitched, melded into a single whine.

A thousand meaningless thoughts pressed upon her mind, sapping, for an instant, her will to act.

Wincing, she pulled away the phone and broke the spell of the sound.

"Ralph?"

Rhea spoke softly.

Unable to face that the smoking, shining apparition on the walkway was her husband.

Unable to face that the uneasiness she'd felt since the car engine had forced itself into existence had now manifested itself in the disfigurement of her husband's sweet face.

She walked the aisle of low hedges lining the walkway toward where Dr. Holm kneeled next to her husband, solemn in his dark suit as a priest administering last rites.

"Is that my *Ralph?!*"

She moved to kneel at Ralph's side as Dr. Holm stood and caught her in the crook of his arm, forcing her upright.

He shook her slightly, fixed her with his dark eyes, and spoke in an urgent whisper. "Don't touch him!"

Then he let go, ran past her toward the house.

From between the fingers of his corrupted hands, Ralph's eyes made contact with hers.

She saw in them a pain she could never have imagined.

Tears welled inside her, choking her words.

"What's the matter?"

Ralph shifted, showed his face.

Rhea tried to hide her shock.

His voice was raw, and carried a tone of abject defeat; each brittle syllable caught in his throat.

"We're . . . not . . . on . . . Earth. . . ."

The sun became brighter.

Harsher.

In the midst of this white glare, a sound at once like the bending of metal and the hiss of a snake came from the sky, filling the air as the buzz of cicadas does on sane summer days.

Rhea looked up.

And saw a layered sky, like the sky she'd seen in the paintings in her mother's Bible, angry as the sky behind Sinai, the churning sky above the golden calf in the great moment of judgment. The light behind the clouds became brighter, as if all the diffuse light collected in a single point.

Light fell from Heaven, in a single shaft, with a thousand banded shades of white within it, as if a prism could create a spectrum of one color. The beam shot toward her feet.

Rhea looked down.

And saw only the fading echo of Ralph, residual in her vision like the echo of bright light at the back of her eye.

A sudden, brutal absence, and Ralph was not there.

The sound faded.

When she felt air moving about her legs to fill the space Ralph had occupied, she knew she was not dreaming.

Voices.

Echoes, as if each word spoken into the phone lines had become a ghost, disembodied, trapped in the thick wires.

The echoes forced their way into Simon's ears.

He wanted to listen, to calm himself with the buzzing irritation, to fixate on it, and so not deal with the wounded man outside.

He'd heard the sound earlier today, as he walked from church.

Andrea spoke at his shoulder, her voice anxious.

"That's the same sound I've been getting all morning, Simon."

He shook off the spell of the sound, looked to her.

"Shall I try one of the other neighbors?" she asked.

"Yes. You'd better."

Andrea ran to the foyer, out the door.

The sound on the line called to him, lulling him to listen again and so find troubling comfort.

Simon slammed down the phone, followed her.

On the walkway, Andrea was holding Mrs. Cashman's arm, reassuringly. They were speaking in sharp, hushed tones. Simon walked to them, followed their gaze to the empty sidewalk.

"Where did he? . . ."

Andrea cut him off, still holding Mrs. Cashman's arm, as if the woman were a child at curbside, being taught how to cross the street.

"She says he disappeared."

Mrs. Cashman had what Simon's jaded colleagues who'd served in Korea called 'the thousand yard stare'; she floated in the twilight realm of numb panic and dumb shock. Her voice carried quiet defeat.

"It's impossible. It has to be."

Simon spoke calmly.

"Did you see where he went?"

"Yes."

"Where?"

"Thin air."

He looked about the street. Why was no one at their windows? Why was no one else outside? Didn't *anyone* hear her scream? Were their neighbors huddled inside, denying that pain and possible death were occurring on their quiet suburban street, paralyzed like the neighbors of Kitty Genovese as she screamed and bled her way to an unattended death?

Mrs. Cashman stared down at the walk.

Simon spoke gently, trying to bring her back to the reality at hand without pushing her toward the panic that seethed just below her numb demeanor.

"He couldn't have gone very far, Mrs. Cashman. I'm afraid something was . . . very wrong with him."

She still stared, transfixed, at the walk.

Simon glanced about the street, the lawn, not wanting to leave Mrs. Cashman's side.

Andrea let out a choked cry, drew Mrs. Cashman closer to her. Simon glanced at Andrea, saw bright fear in her eyes.

He snapped his head over his shoulder to follow Andrea's gaze toward a garage-like shed by the Cashman house.

A shambling shadow.

The sense of pained movement.

A closing door.

The echo of the door slam, hollow in the heated air.

Rhea broke away from Andrea, ran toward the shed. Simon ran to catch her, grabbed her. She struggled to get out of Simon's grip.

"No!! *Let me go to him!!*"

Simon tightened his hold. "Please, Mrs. Cashman!"

"No! Let me go! *Let me go to him!*"

He felt sobs wracking her, felt the wild strength of panic and grief building inside of her that would let her break free and reach her husband and touch whatever contagion had harrowed his flesh.

Andrea grabbed Mrs. Cashman as well, shouting.

"No, Mrs. Cashman! It wasn't him! I *saw* it! It wasn't him! It *wasn't your husband!!*"

Mrs. Cashman stopped struggling, looked toward Andrea.

"It *wasn't!* I saw it." Andrea looked toward Simon, and he saw a fear he'd never seen before in the eyes of his wife. "It wasn't . . . even . . . a man," she said softly.

Andrea had not seen Mr. Cashman up close as he lay on the walk. Had not seen his disfigurement. His twisting pain. The metal protrusions. Ralph might not look like a man at all, half in shadow as he went into the shed.

Simon looked to the shed.

Perhaps Ralph had hidden himself there, to protect his wife from the contagion, to protect her from trying to comfort him and so touch him and his toxicity.

Simon ordered Andrea, as if she were a nurse.

"Bring the car here. We'll take him to the hospital."

Mrs. Cashman seemed lucid, calm. Andrea let go of her and ran across the lawn toward their car in the driveway.

Simon walked toward the shed. Mrs. Cashman tried to follow.

"*No!*" he said. "Stay here!"

Mrs. Cashman shrank back, obeyed him.

Simon walked to the shed across the lawn, beneath the cloak of mist that hung level with the treetops. As he drew near the shed, he smelled something like the skin of cadavers, drifting to him in the windless air. There was an astringent taste on his palate, and a feeling like the tingle of alcohol on the skin as it dries.

He reached the door.

Placed his hand on the latch.

Words . . .

(. . . an electric feeling in his mind, pressing upon his temples; of someone standing at his hind like an ill-wind, yet all around him; the looming intrusion of madness, such as he had only known walking the psychiatric ward in the darkness of deep winter dusk . . .)

. . . forming in his mind, vibrating in the air as if spoken by sharp, wire-thread vocal cords.

"Don't come in!!!"

Words that he heard and felt, that inscribed themselves on his intellect.

The voice behind the door sounded young. The voice *felt* young. Pained. Frightened.

It spoke again from inside the shed, this time more fully in the sane realm of sound and vibration, and less in the skewed grammar of fever dream.

"I'll go away . . . if *you* will."

It was a child's voice, yet heavy with an untrusting inflection Simon had heard only from senile patients refusing medication.

Hand still on the latch, Simon drew a deep breath of tainted air, and spoke slowly.

"Do you need help?"

Heavy silence.

The scent of dead skin.

The feel of his hand on the warm latch, and the new, bitter scent of the sweat of his palm on the brass.

Carefully and slowly, he leaned close to the door and asked of the voice a question to which he knew the answer.

"Is it . . . Mr. Cashman? Ralph?"

"No!"

The single syllable stabbed the air, stabbed his mind like a cold spike.

Then the voice said, again not as intrusively in his mind and more as speech, "Please go away. . . ."

A sense of movement behind him, the sound of tires on pavement.

Simon looked over his shoulder and saw Andrea inching the car forward, parking in front of the Cashman house with the passenger door open. Mrs. Cashman, full of stiff terror, took a step toward the shed.

Simon raised his hand.

"*Stay there!*" he said, trying to not frighten or agitate the . . . person . . . behind the door.

He placed his hand on the latch, brought his face close to the door. He spoke in what felt to be a parody of his bedside manner.

"I'm a doctor. Are you hurt?"

The voice was almost a whisper.

"No."

A pause. Simon heard only his own heartbeat.

Then the voice spoke again, in the choppy way that a person on the verge of tears would.

"Yes. . . . Being afraid hurts."

Simon had treated children who'd been injured while disobeying their parents, doing some dangerous thing in a forbidden place. Finding out what had happened took coaxing; children are more afraid of the consequences of disobedience than they are of the consequences of injury.

"What are you afraid of?"

Still, the quavering of impending tears. Yet now Simon heard a trace of shame in the voice.

"I came through the shield. I'll be punished if I've spoiled the experiment."

Experiment?

Atrocities rose from the dark part of Simon's mind. Cold sweat broke out across his brow; his stomach knotted. What in God's name was he dealing with?

What had hurt Mr. Cashman had likely been a toxic substance. If Ralph had been caught in this . . . experiment . . . this child could also have been exposed. Secondary exposure to the toxin might not be hazardous.

Might not . . .

He'd have to risk secondary exposure.

Simon turned the latch, pushed open the door.

"STAY OUT!!!"

The words struck him with the force of a blow.

Movement, an awkward bound.

The sound of heavy cloth.

In the dim light of the shed, Simon saw the outline of a boy clad in a dark robe. A boy who had grown wrong . . . whose body was misproportioned, like the freaks *comprachicos* once created by putting children in wooden boxes for years at a time, so they would grow to be hunchbacks.

The boy had leapt out of the light from the partly opened door toward the darkened corner. Simon opened the door no further, but could see the boy dimly among the shadows. His indistinct form seemed dusted with a substance that glowed like phosphorous culture stain. The boy bobbed to and fro with jerking, frog-like movements, as if his skeleton and musculature were not joined properly, and he could only relieve the pain by shifting his weight alternately on each malformed leg.

Thalidomide.

The word flashed upon Simon's mind. Yet the boy was far too old to have been exposed in utero, and the extent to which his body was warped seemed to include his very organs, not only his limbs and spine.

An experiment? . . .

For the love of God, an experiment?

The smell of cadaver skin was much stronger.

Simon stood in the partly opened door, just outside the shed. The boy hid among the odds and ends of the Cashmans' life. Piled in the corner where he huddled were pieces of rattan lawn furniture, a rake, a lawn mower, snow shovels, and bags of rock salt.

"Can't I come in and just talk with you?" he asked. "I'd like to hear more about that experiment."

The shadow spoke.

"No. You wouldn't understand, anyway."

The voice seemed hollow, now that Simon did not hear it through the closed door of the shed. The intrusion of the words in Simon's mind abated.

Standing in the doorway, Simon spoke softly, at once to sound soothing, at once to lure the boy into the light so that he might see him better.

"Sometimes doctors understand children better than their parents do."

"I'm *not* a child." The boy shifted his weight with an indignant accent on the word "*not*"—a punctuation in movement, as if movement were the most emphatic way he knew of to communicate a crucial point.

Then, with genuine sadness and regret he said, "I'm sixteen. I'm almost an old man."

The boy, the glimmering shadow, crouched down and rocked, drawing one arm over his head. He drew breath in spastic bursts, in rhythm with his rocking.

"Please let me come in. I promise I. . . ."

"*Your* kind doesn't keep promises." The boy drew his arm from his head, held his hand before his face as if shielding his eyes from bright light.

"My kind? Doctors?"

"*All* of you." Then, Simon could see, even past the dark outline of the boy's shaking hand, that the boy was nodding slightly as he spoke, as if reciting a litany of well-learned indoctrination. "You're untrustworthy, below normal intelligence, undependable, and generally inferior, except physically."

Simon almost smiled at the unthinking naiveté with which the boy spoke. Then nicely, as he'd learned to do while making headway with difficult patients, he said: "It isn't very manly to hide your face while you're trying to give someone an inferiority complex."

He paused, letting his words—his tone—get through.

"Please come on out."

The boy slowed his spastic rocking.

And for an instant, seemed to sit impossibly still as he thought.

Then the rocking began again.

"I will. I'll go back where I came from. But I can't let any of you see me. You're not supposed to. No one is."

Simon realized that he was gripping the door latch so tightly, he might bend it. He relaxed his grip and spoke as calmly as he could.

"All right. I'll go and tell the others to go indoors."

He left the door partly opened and ran back to where Mrs. Cashman stood.

"Go indoors. Quickly."

She was about to object.

He raised his hand.

"Just go! At once!"

She backed toward the doorway of her home.

Simon ran to the car, leaned in through the open passenger side door. Andrea looked at him. He saw in her face the same competence, the same focus, that he had seen when they had first courted. It was the look she had borne whenever she had been working on a tough writing assignment.

"Drive down the street a few yards and wait," he said. "Keep the motor running."

Andrea nodded, turned the ignition.

Simon bounded away from the car as she drove just out of the field of view, passenger side door still open.

Simon looked to the shed, saw the outline of the boy shuffling in the darkness toward the door. The boy placed his hand on the door, pulling it further open, yet still hid himself behind it.

In the hazy light, the hand looked mauled, rough textured like rusted metal, yet shining faintly, as if rubbed with sand that caught bright sun. The knuckles looked as if they had been punched raw, exposing what seemed smooth bone plated with surgical steel. The wrist past the ragged brown cuff of robe looked as if it wore a bracelet that had been melted to the flesh with a blowtorch.

Transfixed by the hand, Simon backed away, out of the boy's line of sight.

In the corner of his eye, he saw Mrs. Cashman standing upon her porch, watching.

He was about to tell her to go inside, when the door to the shed flew open.

A ragged shape leapt to the lawn.

Flayed . . .

The boy had been partly flayed.

Strands of striated muscle showed along his jawline, chromed, as if painted silver. The right cheekbone gleamed beneath the boy's eye.

The boy stopped suddenly, as do trapped animals.

He darted his head about, looking to Simon, to Mrs. Cashman, to Andrea in the car.

He opened his mouth to speak, as if to accuse Simon of betraying him.

And Simon saw that the boy had not been flayed.

The metallic deformities of his face had not been exposed by the peeling away of skin and flesh, but had formed in patterns inscribed by the boy's anatomy, bursting *through* skin as they formed in layers upon tendons, fiber, and bone. Eruptions like silvered glass flecked the boy's brow. His cheek. One moist eyelid. Over parts of the boy's robe, the eruptions had grown through the cloth, protruding like rotted teeth out of diseased gums.

The boy did not speak, but fixed Simon with his eyes. Simon saw in them fear, pain, anger. Then, with impossible speed for so twisted a body, the boy dashed to the car. Simon saw Andrea recoil against the driver's side door as the boy piled in and pulled the passenger door shut.

"TAKE ME BACK!!" he shouted to Andrea, and Simon felt the force of the words in his mind. "OR I'LL *TOUCH* YOU!"

Simon lunged for the car, missing the door handle as Andrea sped down the street.

"No! Andrea! No!"

The car went on—Andrea in the driver's seat, the disfigured boy beside her. From behind, the tableau looked for all the world like a mother driving her son to school.

Simon ran after them in the stifling heat as mist and fog blurred their image in oily gray.

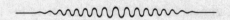

Falling . . .

Out of a state of being more sublime than air, Ralph Cashman fell into materiality, fell into the pain of solidity.

From nothing, he fell into being.

For the instant the light had come down and had taken him apart, he had known the bliss of non-being, a bliss he had only before known in the instant before the coalescence of his consciousness. The collision of the particles of his being inflicted upon him the agony of existence.

He looked about and found himself exiled again to the damnation of choking fog.

Screaming a wail that was absorbed by the fog billowing around him, Ralph Cashman rolled upon his back and wept.

Shapes, crowding around the car in the deep fog.

The door beside her swung open, and Andrea saw a face livid and raw as a harvest moon, peering at her through the haze.

An alien will expressed as voice and unnamable influence urged her to move out of the car.

Cringing, paralyzed, she did not obey.

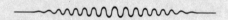

Rhea Cashman knelt on the front walk of her home. The sound, the uncanny sound she had been hearing faintly all this day (like the whine a television makes, even while the volume is off) rang in her ears, punctuating the silence.

She knelt where she had last seen her husband, trying to press her hand into the space he had occupied and perhaps find some tangible evidence that he'd been there at all.

Alone, on a street that she and Ralph had moved to because it had been safe, Rhea drew her arms tight around herself and wept.

A crash.

She started.

Trembling with grief and fear, she stood to see what had made the sound.

A robin lay on the lawn, twitching beneath the living room window.

Another crash, behind her.

She spun to see a sparrow tumble from striking her bedroom window. It thumped to the lawn close to her, and was still.

She looked up and saw a flock of birds circling above. Birds of all types, even a crow cawing among them. With sickening dizziness, she realized that the birds had lost all conception of direction and purpose, as if they had lost their innate sense of true north, their sense of location as defined by the position of the sun.

Ralph's tortured voice echoed in her mind. . . .

"We're . . . not . . . on . . . Earth. . . ."

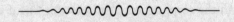

"Andrea!"

Simon stumbled in the fog, as the surface of the road beneath his feet changed. His balance was off, his bearings distorted. He fell through air warm as blood, landed upon soil the color and texture of a scab.

It was slick and glowed faintly, leaving a bright residue on his palms and clothes.

He stood, recoiling from the filth, wiping his hands on his jacket. Ahead, he saw a break in the fog bank, a thinning of the clouds as mist off a harbor thins to reveal the surface of the water. Harsh light beckoned, light such as he had only seen once in the desert noon of Nevada. A growing panic tightened in his chest. This was insane. This was wrong. Straining to hear the motor of the car, to hear any sign of Andrea, he came aware of the sound he'd heard over the phone lines. He wished he could go home, resign himself to hopelessness.

He went forward instead, toward the lighter part of the fog.

And in that place, he found damnation.

The landscape before him was too offensive to fully crowd itself into his sight. It shifted, as if it only partly obtruded into what was knowable by human perception. The terrain was fractured; the skeleton of the world had been forced through its surface, and its wounds steamed faintly, as flesh wounds do in cold air. A huge, looming sun flecked with dark patches turned in the rippling sky. And past the awful white daylight, past the deep violet sky offensively unblue, unfamiliar stars forced their way into visibility. The uneven panorama was dotted with great clumps of crystalline rock that shimmered as does the air above a mirage. He could feel the promise of thunder in the air. The promise of thunder here, where rain could not be knowable, where anything that gave life falling from the sky could not be knowable, made Simon tremble.

The place was a blasphemy.

"God help us . . ." he whispered, wondering if God could hear a prayer uttered beneath a sun and stars so strange and willful and ugly.

He could not leave his wife stranded in this Hell.

He went on. The stones beneath him shifted, clattering in a way that sounded too brittle in the heavy air—as if they struck each other under water. The scab-like soil *yielded* beneath his weight, making him think livid blood might ooze where he placed his heel.

Columns of rock littered the ground, like jutting ribs. The air smelled like the breath of a person stricken with fever. Simon walked on, bearing upon a star shining through the foreign sky that pulsed like a lantern seen through the waving branches of a tree. Several of the large, shimmering clumps he passed were thickly striated with a brown mineral the color of dried blood.

Distance was unknowable, vision distorted in the unrarefied air. Time was immeasurable where an hour had no meaning, where the sun moved wrongly in the sky.

He was alone—without even God looking down from the Heaven beneath which Simon belonged.

He would not find Andrea here. He would find only a misery and an ugliness that would kill his soul a small bit with each step. Stopping a moment, undoing his tie, loosening his shirt, Simon thought of going back, getting help, *demanding* help from his neighbors who had hidden themselves while Ralph Cashman collapsed before his home.

And in that moment, he became aware of movement behind him . . . of something at his back that touched his mind the way the voice of the trapped boy had.

He spun around.

A clump of the shimmering rock, some steps behind him, glimmered in the ugly sunlight. The striations of brown caught the light as well, reflected it in patches as do the scales of butterfly wings. Once he and Andrea had gone to a museum and had seen roughly hewn expressionist statues that looked vaguely like the clump now in his sight. The distortion of his sense of distance had grown worse . . . he had passed this clump perhaps twenty paces ago. Yet it now seemed no more than ten paces away.

Simon turned and went forward, bearing upon the star that pulsed in the firmament before him, in a sky the dark and ugly purple of a deep scar. He would turn back, soon, if he found nothing. He would turn back before the heat and the assault this world inflicted upon his senses overwhelmed him.

The sense of intrusion reasserted itself in his mind.

Simon swung around.

They might have once been men.

Slowly, ploddingly, two robed figures moved toward him—with skin as translucent in parts as that on the brow of a newborn, calcified flesh bursting through. Their faces were swollen, warped, as if they had been cast in clay and then crushed and pulled into sickening travesties of human features. They glimmered with phosphorus dust. Splotches of metal, rounded like cysts, clung to their hands and faces. Their inner anatomy—bone and ligament and tendon and vein—was partly expressed upon their skin in dull chrome-like layerings.

The stink of cadaver skin brought gorge to his throat.

Simon turned and ran.

And saw a hand emerge from the clump of stone before him. The folds of the clump, the small overhangs, began to move. To quiver. The hand, shimmering, with metal ligaments striping its back and fingers, moved with the laziness of a sea-fan as an arm unfolded from the contours of the stone around it.

A face pulled itself away from the stone.

The striations of brown fell into the drape of a robe as the clump rose to its full height and walked toward him.

Simon felt the other two behind him, felt their presence itch upon his mind as the one before him forced its way into his thoughts.

The breath he drew to scream felt heavy as hot water in his lungs.

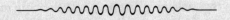

Shapes.

Milling in the distance, barely visible past her transparent tomb. The shapes blended against the background of the onyx and gray walls of the stone chamber they stood within.

Andrea called, struck the glass coffin that confined her. There was silence, as if the air within the glass refused to transmit sound. Her hands left no prints. She breathed as if within a vacuum—with aching emptiness in her lungs.

The twisted boy who had forced his way into the car loped toward the glass, seeming self-conscious of his mutilated face as a boy in the sane world would be of acne. His eyes were bright with curiosity, drinking in her nakedness as if it were an unimaginable spectacle. He hopped about the coffin, trying to view all of her, trying to capture all of her with his gaze.

The non-air in the coffin *changed.* It caught of the light an unnamable color—at once claret-red and the iridescent orange visible only in rainbows. The new gas swirled around her in a thick cloud, shifting to gold.

It clung to her skin and hair as does heavy, thick sweat.

She could not hold her breath long enough.

They herded him.

The two sickening lampoons of the human form behind him and the one ahead directed him through a contorted world, the doodle-work of an autistic god. They did not speak. Simon saw through rips in their robes the mottled and enfolded flesh of their torsos. They walked as if cast in hardened mud. Within the folds of flesh nestled bright protrusions: things like boils that looked as if they could be lanced to yield quicksilver.

Simon had tried to run from the shambling hulks. As he ducked aside, one of the beings merely held out its arm, as if about to cradle him. Simon looked at the thing's fingers, its hand that had been skinned from within. He thought of Ralph, the stricken boy.

He dared not risk their touch.

Resigning himself, Simon walked on.

Here, in the mad landscape, was a cliff of translucent gray crystal. It held scores of shades of gray, some of which Simon was sure had never been seen by the human eye before. Within the cliff and its unthinkable grays was a thick streak of clarity, like a refracted shaft of light through murky waters.

In the distance a few paces later Simon could see a knoll like a billowing storm cloud, settled to the ground and made solid as stone, littered with clustergrowths of tendrils like the frayed strands of copper cable.

Ahead was a frozen cataract of glassy stone.

The part of Simon's mind that longed for the world he knew heard the roar of a waterfall as they neared it.

Simon and the beings passed through a door-like space between two still "streams" of stone.

Inside was a dark place, vast. Quiet. At once like an ancient coliseum, tiered in concentric ledges; at once like a cathedral of dim glass and ribbed granite, vaulting to a ceiling almost completely hidden in darkness. Columns of rock, large as redwoods, curved from the floors to almost touch high above, like the clutching fingers of giant hands coming together to grasp one another.

Upon the ledges were layer upon layer of great hunched gargoyles that looked as if they had been fashioned of melted wax and pewter.

Alive . . .

Lumpy distortions of human-like beings, clothed in rags and fixed to the ledges like stalagmites—immobile brothers to the things that had herded Simon. Their eyes moved. *Only* their eyes moved.

This place was more stifling than outside. The heat rested on his neck and back like a damp cloak, and Simon realized, as the stink of cadaver flesh brought him close to blacking out, that he felt radiant body heat. Through hundreds of thick glimmering faces, he saw, he *felt,* the eyes of the beings focus upon him.

The silence was shattered.

A cacophony of voices, shrill, like silver-voiced birds articulating words, resonant in the chamber as the calls of gulls echoing against a cliff face. Simon felt their vibration in the air, in his mind. It was a form of the sound he had heard on the street, and over the dead telephone lines. The three beings who had brought him corralled him toward a high bench near the center of the structure.

Three lumps of craggy stone-flesh sat upon the bench, naked. Each seemed to have a single leg from the knee up, one limb melded from two, branching from the point where their bodies had fused to the bench.

One being, in the center, sat slightly higher than the other two.

The bright cacophony went on.

From the high, vaulted ceiling, where the tips of the giant stone fingers seemed to almost touch, an intense, heated light fell upon Simon, blinding him, making his skin feel as if it would blister.

And as his eyes readjusted, he saw clearly the glimmering shapeless faces of the three who sat upon the bench. Their eyes shone like black gems set deep in quilts of puffy flesh and metallic protrusions. Here and there a wisp of hair or beard grew sadly, shining like spun silver wire.

The one seated higher than the other two—whom Simon took to be the authority of this place—spoke loudly; the movement of the Authority's lips was as unsettling as seeing the two edges of a wound form words.

"*STOP!*" he called to the still congregation.

The cacophony went on.

"*STOP!*"

Simon heard the Authority's voice in his mind, strong and slow. Focused. The opposite of the boy's panicked intrusion.

"*STOP!*"

The cacophony dimmed.

"*STOP!*"

There was silence.

Slowly, with great and painful effort, the Authority leaned forward and angled his black crystalline eyes down upon Simon. Within the facets of the eyes, Simon saw the remnants of pupils, the smear of ruined irises.

The Authority asked in a slow, heavy tone, "Do you know where you are?"

Simon swallowed, tried to focus in the withering heat of the light.

"Nowhere on . . . Earth."

The still beings, molded upon their concentric tiers, laughed in resonant vibrations like music. The sound washed over the place as does a crashing wave.

The Authority's voice was a bit louder in Simon's mind, sweeping across his awareness. His physical voice stayed steady in tone and pitch.

"You are on the hot, greedy star we call Luminos. It sweats just outside your admirable galaxy."

Simon pondered this impossibility.

And knew it to be the only possibility of what he faced.

"How . . . did we get here?"

Again, the swift bright music of inhuman laughter.

Again, the silence.

The Authority blinked with painful slowness.

"Teleportation," he said.

Simon turned the word over in his mind, tried to fathom the means by which a word he was unfamiliar with could be articulated in thought and voice by beings who could not know his tongue.

"Teleportation?"

A smug movement. A cocking of the Authority's head in a degree measurable in millimeters, almost as unnoticeable as the movement of leaves on a day of soft winds.

"As your television cameras transmit images, so ours, refined and advanced, of course, transmit brute matter."

Simon felt a cold sickness in his belly.

Felt a despair he could not have imagined feeling while his intellect was joined to his living body.

The Authority went on.

"While you and your neighbors slept, we borrowed, so to speak, six square city blocks of earth, disassembling the atoms there, reassembling them here. Naturally, we did not intend for you to become aware of our experiment until it was concluded. Experiments are best conducted on the blithely ignorant."

The breaking of atoms . . . the destruction of matter.

The transmission of human beings, perhaps as a focused beam.

Flesh made light, made a puzzle of jumbled particles solved in an instant.

But what of the instant in which the puzzle was not solved?

Simon became weak in the knees as he glanced about the arena, at the sickening beings who had become one with their landscape.

He met the gaze of the Authority again and asked, "What kind of experiment?"

The Authority pursed his wound-mouth.

"Watch," he said. "We shall exhibit the full extent of our physical mobility."

The three beings on the high bench shifted, only slightly. From their swollen limbs came the sound of creaking, as of stone before it is split. A moment of this, and just perceptibly, the tribunal ceased their aching attempt at movement.

"We do not begin life as we end it," said the Authority. "Luminoid children, at birth, are as yours—sweet golden nuggets in the palm of Fate's hand." The Authority narrowed his eyes, and Simon saw the silvery needle-glimmer of his eyelashes. "But the hot organism is in the genes, and soon, all too soon, while still in the cock-a-hoop dawn of their maturity, the eruptions begin. And all Luminoids celebrate their majority in places like this."

Simon glanced above and behind the tribunal to the tiers of vaguely human outlines, who shifted their misshapen forms only slightly. He breathed air thick with the taint of flesh.

"Like . . . this?"

"We call such places Contemplative-Energy Plants. We elders sit here, doomed, immobile, unable to do anything but think; and there is our compensation! Since no single fraction of life-energy is wasted on meaningless movement, all energy, all the mad monstrous force of it, is made available to the mind. Can you comprehend the scope and skill of minds that are never drained, never dulled . . . minds like transcendent birds soaring to the most splendoured dreamings of the Universe?"

Simon forsook so Faustian an imagining.

"I cannot conceive of such minds sanctioning the abduction of innocent people."

The Authority gave a light laugh, barely audible as the single note of a distant chime.

"Nothing is so modifiable as morality," he said, as if explaining one of the most minor of life's injustices to a child. "The Abduction Act was passed in a state of Emergency . . . a state which, on this planet as on yours, excuses a multitude of high-level apostasies."

The gargoyles in the unmoving arena laughed briefly, and somewhat dutifully.

The Authority went on.

"Until recently, our youngsters produced the end products of our dreams. But now they rebel. And we are helpless. And there is so much work to be done."

The full implication, the full insult of what the Authority was saying struck Simon in a wave of nausea and fury.

"You've brought us here to do your work for you?"

"We are studying the feasibility of it. If your small test group survives this sultry clime. . . ."

"And if none of us becomes infected."

"We're fairly positive that our immunization techniques will work," said the Authority. Simon recognized the tone as that he and his colleagues used when they wished to placate patients. "That veil of gas-clouds you wandered through is little more than a deterrent, similar to those brick and mortar things you erect on earth. But the humming you hear, *that* is what will keep you strong and useful. As anyone who has listened to a great and demonic speaker will tell you, sound waves can reach and subjugate the most recalcitrant organism."

The Authority paused, as if speaking at such length were a great effort.

"In a few days, perhaps sooner, we'll know if we've made any mistakes, or any miracles. . . ."

"You've already failed! My next door neighbor—"

The Authority cut Simon off.

"Yes. He was a lesson to us. We were only trying to keep him from going back and betraying everything prematurely. And we saw that contagion does occur, when one of us touches one of you. . . ."

The Authority's wound-mouth made the shadow of a smile.

"I doubt there will be much of that! Barring any other infeasibilities, we will soon abduct the rest of you. *All* of you. All the brutes that plow that brutal star called 'Earth.'"

"*We* can rebel, too."

"You?" said the Authority. "Vain fleshmen who love their *bodies* above all else that nature has given them?! No . . . you will obey. At the threat of our touch, you will obey!"

The Authority laughed. Again, like a single note of a chime heard from far away.

"And you will be happy, here. Your lives will be comfortable and secure. You will be free to worship and love and to think . . . as haphazardly as usual."

"What if some of us do become infected? Even if we aren't touched by you?"

A slight shifting of craggy flesh beneath the Authority's eyes—the hint of the look upon a man's face as he raises his hand to his chin to ponder a problem.

"Then you won't be able to work," said the Authority. "You'll be as we are. We shall consider the project infeasible, and turn our minds and instruments on other lively planets. There *are* others, you know."

The Authority leaned back a few fractions of an inch, moved his gaze ever so slightly away from Simon's.

"Go, now. A guide will show you through the fog. Tell your neighbors to fear no fears, and dream no dreams of escape. For there is no escape."

Simon did not move, nor speak.

He felt the itch of the still beings' wonderment that he did not obey the Authority outright.

"Go!" said the Authority, and Simon felt the weight of decades of thought and *will*.

"Where is my wife?" Simon asked softly.

"She will be returned to you. Quite soon."

"Where is she?"

"GO!"

Simon looked about, seeking some escape, some way to break free and search for Andrea in this Hell inconceivable billions of miles from the world God had created for him to live upon. The entrance to the chamber was blocked by the shuffling forms of his captors, those still able to move. In anger and fear, Simon shouted, "*Where is my wife?!!*"

The sense of wonderment from the beings around him changed to a sense for which Simon had no name . . . at once anger and disgust and admiration that *he* dare to express *will* before the Authority.

The Authority addressed the three who had escorted Simon. "Take him back!"

One of the guardians raised its arm, moving silently forward. As it entered the column of brilliant light that encircled Simon, he saw that it had no mouth; the eruptions had fused its lips together. It herded Simon toward the door. Its two companions joined them as they went back toward the wall of the silent cataract.

The clusters of still Luminoids watched from their perches, following them with their gazes to the extent which their stiffened bodies would allow. As Simon passed through the entrance to the surreal patchwork landscape of Luminos, he pondered what the Authority had said, pondered the suspicion that was making his heart an empty shadow in his breast.

The act of teleportation was murder. The body Simon now had was but a copy of the one that had been disintegrated.

Knowing that he was dead, knowing that the vessel of his spirit had been obliterated in the moment that it was broken to atoms, he wondered among what stars his soul now drifted.

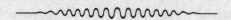

A shape.

Andrea walked along the stolen street where sat her stolen home, a home she had been desperate to leave, which now offered her her only possibility of comfort and security.

Under the harsh diffused sunlight, she cast no shadow.

She wondered if any neighbors could see her from their windows, a formless apparition. A ghost.

A mere shape . . . ambulatory.

As she reached for the shining brass knob of her front door, she saw the radiance from her hand reflect off of it, spreading in a corona.

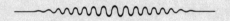

Ralph Cashman stood.

The grinding in his joints was audible.

As he walked, he felt a scab of mirror break upon the skin of his back.

The fog wrapped him in gauze the color of the moon's face.

He nearly blacked out with the first step he took.

There was no night.

Simon felt night in his heart, felt an ache for darkness, or at least the neglected beauty of a sunset. But the sun of Luminos had reached its zenith. A terrible alien noon. Even the star that had guided him could no longer be seen in the livid purple sky. The three silent mockeries drove him across the sick panorama. The translucent rock, the transparent soil,

were now without the small mercy of shadow, their
shadings transformed from dead grays into the muted
whites of dirty snow, an affront to his longing for
coolness in this brutal, dehumanizing heat.

Simon Holm, a healer, now dead and resurrected
by his murderers, driven across a damned landscape
Satan might forsake as unworthy to rule, pondered
the notion of the soul. Was the soul energy? Or was it
contained in the matrix of neurons and synapses?
Was he, a man reassembled, a man without a soul?

His voiceless escorts brought him through the fog
boundary to his neighborhood.

With the threat of a touch, one of them gestured
him toward the stolen street. The sight of the familiar
houses shocked him, hurt his eyes.

When he'd stumbled home, he climbed the stairs,
weakly gripping the banister, intent on reaching his
bedroom, intent on stealing sleep. Intent on mourn-
ing Andrea in dark dreams.

As he swung open the bedroom door, he heard
soft whimperings. Sobs. Light came from the bedroom, like the familiar afternoon light of the sun.

Andrea stood before him.

A ghost.

Her image was impressed upon the air around
her, shifting, transparent, like the reflection on a window on a sunny day. It clung to her, moved with her,
shuddering as she sobbed. As she cried within it, the
image glowed, a corona shedding dull gold light. It
struck the mirror above the bureau, making a double
illumination, casting double shadows.

"Andrea?"

She raised her hand from within her shining twin, crying, unable to talk. She shook her head, slightly, and the double shadows danced.

Simon stepped toward her.

She took a step back. The double shadows shifted, making Simon dizzy.

"Stay away, Simon!"

Simon obeyed.

"A while longer. They told me this would fade, soon."

"What . . . is it?"

"A gas."

Then, very quietly, she said, "A sterilizing gas."

The glow faded, slightly. The shadows deepened.

Simon looked at her, puzzled.

"The boy didn't touch me, but we were so close in that closed car. We breathed the same air. They thought I should be sterilized, as a precautionary measure."

The shadows deepened more.

"It seems to be fading," he said.

Andrea raised her arms before her eyes. The glow dimmed. Her twin image settled, shifted, began to join itself to the solidity of her form.

"Oh . . . yes. And it's odorless. And painless. And. . . ." With a fresh welling of tears in her voice, she said, "They use it to control the growth of their population."

The glow faded to nothing as she brought her hands to her face and turned away from Simon.

As she turned, the import of what she said struck him.

"Oh . . . my poor darling."

The cadaver smell.

The desolation of this planet.

The immobility of the adult "Luminoids," those who would be capable of reproduction.

"*The hot organism is in the genes,*" the Authority had said.

The dual meaning of 'sterilization.'

Andrea, back to him, sobbed into her hands.

"I wanted our children to inherit a better Earth," she said. "Now, there will be no children."

"And no Earth," said Simon. "Not even a bad one to bring children into."

Andrea turned. As she brought her hands away from her face, Simon saw that her wedding ring had been tarnished by the gas, the gold made a dull iron color.

"No Earth?"

"If we survive, they'll bring up every capable, able-bodied human being alive. Perhaps even the old and useless. . . . They'll need millions of us. As laborers. To manufacture *their* dreams."

The fear and sadness in her eyes gave way to bright indignation, to rage.

"We can't let them abduct the whole human race, Simon! We can't!"

He said nothing.

His thoughts were of the infection of this planet, airborne, yet '*in the genes.*' Of beings unable to move, let alone reproduce in the way their vaguely human form would suggest. Of the smell of flesh and ambient proteins about their captors.

Genetic transmission of a disease neutralized by a *gas*.

Genetic transmission—airborne.

Their captors reproduced this way. The disease—transmitted to humans *definitely* by touch, *perhaps* by breathing the same air—was a by-product of their paralyzed reproduction. Their immobility would allow for no other mode of reproduction and genetic transmission. The eruptions were the by-product of some twisted alien veneer. . . .

"What can we *do*, Simon?"

Simon met her eyes, saw the selfless fire that burned within them.

"*Do?* To stop the abduction of the whole human race?"

"Yes!"

"Nothing!" he said. Then he regretted showing such despair before what burned in Andrea's eyes. "Can you think of a way?"

"No," she said. Her hands, close to her chest, balled into fists. "But one of us might! Or all of us together might!"

"The only advantage we have over them is our mobility, Andrea. But there's nowhere we can *run*."

"Not run!" She drew her fists away from her chest, held them ready at her sides. "Not run! *Fight! Resist!*"

She stepped close to him. He could almost feel the beat of her heart, her fervor. He took her in his arms, as he had ached to do for so many weeks, now.

"Forgive me, Andrea."

"Forgive you, Simon? Why?"

Her breath touched his face. Their closeness healed some long aching part of him he had been keeping closed off.

"For trying to put out that spirit in you. I . . . I didn't understand."

She kissed him.

And Simon Holm and the woman he adored found comfort in a night of their own creation, holding each other, in the sane and decent act of lovemaking.

The cries were like a child's.

Ralph stumbled toward the distorted sound.

The light had taken him apart. The things that had abducted them, had batted him away from Rhea as a cruel child bats away an ant.

Something ground in his knee with each step.

The cries became more distinct.

A darker shape in the swirling fog, small, low to the ground.

Ralph stooped before it.

It was a young calico cat.

Maybe it had wandered away from the street it had known, hoping to go to some field where it could mouse and catch birds and find its way back to its owners before dusk. But instead of finding a field, it had found this desolation.

It cried again, plaintive and sad.

Ralph reached for the cat, who walked slowly, cautiously within his grasp.

He didn't want to infect it, but he did want to help.

He began to take off his jacket, to wrap the cat in it. The jacket was covered in glimmering contagion and was scored, as if the fog were partly dissolving it. But the silk lining was intact . . . he could see it, whole, through the open patches in the outer fabric.

He screamed as he pulled off the jacket.

When he came to, the cat was gone.

The eruptions had grown through the shirt in places. In other places torn skin and abrasions showed through holes in his shirt. On the lining of his jacket were eruptions that had been upon his skin, stuck fast, bits of cotton and skin clinging to them.

Taking off his jacket had pulled them from his flesh.

Staring at the jacket, Ralph felt something inside him quietly snap.

———∿∿∿∿∿∿∿∿∿∿∿∿∿———

Drifting in the gray realm between sleep and wakefulness, Andrea felt Simon's gaze.

Then, the soft coolness of a satin comforter laid gently upon her. She felt its smoothness, its suppleness, through the silk of Simon's robe. The fine textures kept at bay the moist heat, providing a warmth like the touch of a human body, not the feverish weight of the foreign air.

Simon took a few steps toward the door.

"I'm awake, Simon," she said.

Simon knelt next to the bed. The look of love in his eyes filled her with a fresh hurt, a fresh longing for the world they'd been taken from.

Simon's expression became dark, as if he were thinking of a terminally ill patient.

"There's no way to fight them, Andrea."

She turned to look toward the earthly tree just outside their window and the unearthly sky above it.

She met his eyes again, breathed deeply of the wonderful scent of his body, close to her. "No."

"I love you."

"I didn't want to leave you."

"I gave you no choice."

And some grave thought etched itself upon his face. His brow furrowed, and his dark expression was eclipsed by what could only be called a flash of revelation.

"That's the whole bright mystique of life, Andrea, isn't it? Choice. Maybe that's what the soul is. Choice."

"Can we live with the loss of it?"

"Perhaps. But it would be better to die trying to win it back."

He stood. But even in his stillness, Andrea could see by his stance that his mind was racing, that some fire had been sparked inside him.

Andrea rose, stood beside him.

"I'll go from door to door," he said. "'*Six square blocks,*' he said. I'll explain, if anyone still needs explanations. And we'll meet somewhere, all of us. And work something out."

A stirring in her heart.

She saw now, for the first time in long months, the spirit that had first drawn her to this man, the spirit that he himself had held at bay since they had married. She walked toward the bureau, began to take off Simon's robe so she could dress and go with him door to—

. . . shining luminescence, budding upon her shoulder . . .

. . . catching light the way the silk of the robe did . . .

. . . when she saw it in the mirror, she felt its stiffness, its inflexibility upon her skin . . .

. . . felt its heaviness in her flesh, touching her very collarbone . . .

Simon stepped behind her.

Quickly, she pulled the robe over her shoulders.

"Where shall we meet?" he asked.

Dark concern crossed his face.

"What is it, Andrea?"

She pulled the robe tight around her, feigning a sudden chill.

"I don't know."

He stepped closer.

"What is it? What's the matter?"

She withdrew from him, half a step, and gave him a half-hearted smile.

"Suddenly I feel bad, Simon. Frightened. Suddenly, it's all hitting me. Go on, Simon. Go. Door to door."

"Will you come with me?"

"I'll meet you . . . wherever all of you will meet."

"Where?"

"The church?"

Simon thought a moment, then gave a slight nod.

"The church."

As Andrea heard his footsteps on the stairs she stepped close to the mirror, pulled back the robe.

Two more buds of luminescence: a small one near her upper arm, a smaller one at the side of her throat. They felt like pinpricks on her skin. As she swallowed, she could feel the deep roots of the blotch upon her neck scrape against the inside of her throat.

She pulled the robe high, tight against her neck.

Andrea stood before the mirror, eyes shut tightly against tears, with the posture of a martyr in an icon.

Church bells.

The broken man once named Ralph Cashman heard church bells, in the endless fog.

Hoarsely, he called his wife's name . . . the harsh, broken glass sound of his own voice frightening him.

With thrusting, brute energy, he walked toward the peal of the bells.

Ignoring the pain of talking, ignoring the pain of movement, he called Rhea's name over and over in the unhearing mist.

Rhea took comfort in following.

Her neighbors, shuffling before her, behind her, filed toward the Church of the Immaculate Conception. The church bells rang, creating a beautiful resonance, despite the muffling air. Their ringing drowned out the whine that she'd been hearing all this terrible, unending day.

Rhea did not know so many people lived near her. She had not seen them outside their homes, walking at night, carrying groceries, sitting on porches on the nights of hot summers. She'd seen only cars moving down the streets of their safe neighborhood, so brutally unlike the close neighborhoods of the city. Seeking safety, she had found isolation.

The man walking beside her had emerged from a house not fifty yards from her own. She had never seen his face before.

Rhea's neighbors were all she now had. By the simple virtue of their responding to Dr. Holm's summons, and going door to door themselves, they had vindicated themselves in a small way. They were no longer held by the paralysis that had kept them from coming to help Ralph.

Rhea felt comfort in following.

She filed with her neighbors into the church.

She had never been in a place of worship so large. Only the pews closest to the doors were filled. Mostly, her neighbors, her scores of unfamiliar neighbors, hung tightly near the entrances, or stood in the wide center aisle. Candles were lit everywhere. An old, bearded man and his small wife looked about the church, craning their necks. The old man wore a yarmulke, the woman a scarf over her head. In many people's hands were rosaries, glinting in the amber light.

In this unfamiliar church, she walked toward a bank of candles, wanting to light one in prayer for her Ralph.

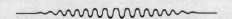

Andrea fixed her scarf about her neck as she walked, trying to hide the silvery eruptions. She went toward the church, toward the tolling bells. In the heavy heat, the eruptions were oddly cool on her skin, like a scrape that is not quite bad enough to bleed, yet deep enough to feel cold in the open air.

Her eyes cast downward, she did not see Ralph Cashman step from behind a young oak, most of his visible skin glinting of metal, textured in patches like the bark of the tree itself. He bled through a splay of holes in his shirt.

She looked up and made eye contact with him, seeing a hunted, hurt look like that of addicts in halfway houses.

Something had been shattered in him.

He grabbed her, tight, about the shoulders. His palms burned with a heat sickeningly unlike fever.

Ralph shook her; she gave a small yell.

"Where's Rhea?" he said, his voice grating like coarse sand.

He stopped shaking her. Dimly in her fear, she wondered if he had reinfected her, doubling the exposure she'd suffered from the boy.

She met his eyes again, trying to speak, to reassure.

As she looked into his eyes, she saw them crust over with an ice-like film.

He shook her again.

"Where's Rhea?!"

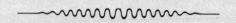

Simon looked about the church, at the icons, the stained glass.

He had, throughout his life—even in his deepest and strongest moments of devotion—felt removed from the grace of saints in churches, separated by the centuries that stood between him and the martyrs of his faith.

Now, he was separated from them not only by time, but by uncountable billions of miles.

Is Grace limited by the physics of light? he thought. *We, who have been stolen from Earth, must have traveled as light. Yet faster than light. Perhaps we traveled through a hole in space that allows for the passage of light not limited by the laws of physics. How else could our captors have known about us? The light seen by them would be of an Earth from the distant past, before the creation of Man, their intended slaves. Can Grace travel as light? Could it have been carried with us across the stars?*

He turned his gaze away from the still, frozen saints of glass and stone above him to the people milling in the church. They were quiet, the silence that overcomes a group faced with a common emergency.

Andrea had not come.

Cold sweat slicked his palms.

Father Fontanna was greeting what must have been the last arrivals; the church was nearly full. The priest turned toward Simon.

Simon saw insight and understanding in the old man's eyes. Father Fontanna moved close to Simon and whispered, with a surety that only Simon's confessor could have: "Don't worry. She'll be here."

A thunderous noise.

Three burly men were closing the great church doors, then positioning themselves against the entrance like self-appointed sentinels.

"*No!*" said Father Fontanna. "We close our doors to no one!"

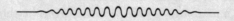

Ralph Cashman seemed to calm, hanging his head low, ashamed that he'd touched Andrea, that he had exposed her. He seemed responsive to her words, her explanation of what they all faced, and how they planned to deal with it.

Andrea stopped trying to hold him back.

He jerked his head, his eyes glinting with panic beneath the ice-like formations that lay metastasized upon them.

"*No!*" he said in his coarse voice. "No! I don't believe you!"

He broke away.

Andrea heard the rattle of his brittle lungs.

"Rhea!" he called to the empty street, loping toward the tolling bells.

Andrea followed, unable to keep pace with the desperate man. Ralph moved with the same speed that the twisted boy had.

They were not reaching their neighbors.

Simon and Father Fontanna stood on the altar steps near the pulpit, trying to stem the tide of panic and anger and fear. Few had taken to the pews. Most had chosen to stand, to pace, to mill and whisper and mumble, or to huddle close with their loved ones.

At the far end of the church, the three husky men leaned against the church doors in defiance of Father Fontanna. Rhea Cashman stood in the alcove some steps away from the men, staring at lit candles, hands clasped in prayer.

Simon spoke again.

"Please! Believe me! They don't intend to hurt us! Not physically! They *want* us strong and well! They need our strength!"

The whisperings grew, heavy and sibilant. A woman brought her kerchief to her brow, rubbing it across her temple with spastic movements. A young man began to rock back and forth as he gripped the back of a pew. Another man brought his hands over his ears and cast his head downward, nodding his head in small jerks.

Their individual fears would make collective action impossible. . . .

Infeasible.

The mutterings of the crowd, the sea of voices, were like the sounds of their captors' Contemplative-Energy Plant.

Simon looked to Father Fontanna.

Wordlessly, expressionlessly, the priest assumed the pulpit.

He raised his powerful voice.

"Our Father, who art in Heaven . . ."

Father Fontanna stumbled upon the word 'Heaven,' which here, in this perdition among the stars, seemed so vague and distant an idea. Simon looked toward the makeshift congregation.

Gradually, they fell quiet.

". . . hallowed be Thy Name. . . ."

Gradually, glances turned toward the pulpit.

"Thy Kingdom come, Thy Will be done . . ."

Gradually, the small, nervous, hopeless tension abated. The change was like that of sunlight breaking over a field.

". . . on Earth, as it is in Heaven."

A stumble on the word 'Heaven,' again. But this time, the pause was one of collecting hope, invoking the strength of the transcendent idea behind the word. A few people in the crowd mouthed the words of the prayer.

"Give us this day our daily bread, and forgive us our trespasses, as we forgive those who trespass against us . . ."

The threat of panic no longer hung in the air; Simon felt free of its oppressive weight. He also felt, for the first time in long years, the soft beauty of the prayer.

". . . and lead us not into temptation, but deliver us from evil."

Father Fontanna bowed his head as he took a breath; speaking the prayer had clearly drained him.

"Amen," he said.

"Amen," said the congregation, though not in unison. Simon spoke his as a quietly exhaled breath, barely more than a whisper.

As the echo of the last "Amen" faded from hearing, a pounding at the door. . . .

His neighbors turned silently from the pulpit toward the door.

The moment of peace was gone.

The pounding at the door went on.

Andrea?

Those closest to the doors backed away, save for the three burly men, who braced themselves against the doors.

Father Fontanna's voice rang out from the pulpit.

"Open the door!"

A few shocked murmurs and complaints. The big men did not obey.

Pounding.

Simon walked down the altar steps.

"Please," he called to the men. "It's my wife."

Father Fontanna stepped down from the pulpit, brushed past Simon, walked silently toward the doors. The crowd parted for him, stepping back to the spaces between the pews. Simon followed, the crowd closing behind him as he and the priest neared the door.

Pounding.

Simon stood at Father Fontanna's shoulder as he faced the self-appointed guards. The Father, small, old, and frail before the burly men, conveyed neither anger nor criticism.

Pounding, falling quiet.

The priest raised his hand to move the men aside with a movement like that of giving benediction. Tilting their heads as if they carried a small shame, the men stepped away, joining the rest of the crowd.

Fontanna grabbed hold of the big bronze latch, pulled open the heavy doors.

A once human thing stood there, in the glare of alien light.

Arms upraised, face twisted . . . glittering, shimmering with luminescence. Distorted and swollen, with metal eruptions making surface-shadows of his jaw and cheekbones. Hardened lymph, like candle-drippings, on his skin. Eyes like black gems, many-faceted in their quartz-like irregularity. Wounds, like those of multiple gunshots, showing through ragged holes in his shirt.

Simon smelled the familiar, ugly cadaver smell; behind him, he felt the clamor of the congregation, the charge in the air of heavy shock, of horror. He heard cries, raised voices, a scatter of footfalls, backing away.

But he did not turn away.

Ralph's wounds had ravaged his soul and his mind. The torture of infection had broken him, stolen most of his dignity.

By turning his back Simon would take what shred of dignity Ralph Cashman still possessed.

Father Fontanna stood by Simon, palms raised in a gesture of quiet welcome.

Ralph's face twisted, trying to give expression to pain and anger and fear. His arms dropped, his shoulders dropped.

Over the fading sounds of panic and fear, Simon heard the leatherine creak of Ralph's skin as his mouth turned downward in a slow grimace; the beginnings of painful sobs came deep from his chest. Tears fell from his crystalline eyes. Simon had never seen illness or injury inflict such humiliation and defeat.

Father Fontanna went to Ralph, hands still extended, offering solace to the man suffering grotesque stigmata on the church threshold.

Simon took hold of Father Fontanna's shoulder, pulled him back gently. "*Careful, Father,*" he mouthed, more than whispered.

Father Fontanna glanced at Simon, who cocked his head toward the crowd. The older man's tired eyes were understanding; he knew who stood before him in the doorway.

"Tell them," whispered Simon.

The priest nodded. The congregation was now a wall of humanity, pressed together, whispering in counterpoint to Ralph's sobs. Simon remembered treating a man on the streets of Chicago who had been struck by a car. As he had knelt in the crosswalk, he'd glanced up to see a similar wall of faces and bodies joined by collective immobility.

The priest brought his hands together—the same gesture he made before opening his arms to read scripture.

Silence took the church, the instant of unmovable quiet that precedes a reading. Ralph stopped sobbing, in response, perhaps, to the quieting of the anxious whispers.

Simon, for the first time, knew the silence from outside the congregation; he saw the faces of those assembled, saw the quiet visible in their eyes, in their posture. Even the three men who had stood guard at the door now dwelled in the quiet, standing within the wall, touched by pity for the man they had tried to keep out.

Father Fontanna's voice, firm yet gentle, did not break the silence, but parted it.

"This man, who does nothing and still strikes fear in your hearts. . . . He is your neighbor. His name is Ralph Cashman."

A new fit of Ralph's sobs punctuated the priest's words, as if his name had awakened his pain. They reverberated in the church, amid the high rafters, against the stained glass mosaics of saints, over the high sconces upholding the stations of the cross.

Movement in the crowd.

A parting of the human wall.

A lone figure came out of its ranks.

Rhea Cashman slowly walked the aisle of the church toward her wounded husband.

"*Ralph?*" she said softly.

She moved slowly, with sorrow.

Simon stood between the broken man and his wife, next to Father Fontanna.

As Ralph heard Rhea speak his name, he stopped sobbing and drew several long breaths. Some part of him emerged from behind his veil of suffering and found expression in his mutilated eyes.

Rhea neared Ralph; her steps quickened. She was about to give him her hand. . . .

As reflex, Simon stepped forward to prevent Rhea from exposing herself to contagion. Before he could reach her, Ralph backed away and said, "*No! Don't touch me!*"

She stopped short.

Man and wife huddled by the church door. Ralph's face was pleading; the look on Rhea's face could at once be called pleading and comforting.

The congregation watched mutely, their faces tense, immobile as death masks. Yet everyone still partly held the look they had at the moment when silence had taken the church. Some clutched prayer books and Bibles, raised absently to their chests. Rosaries glinted in the unearthly light falling from the windows. Slowly, the wall of unmoving humanity broke apart. Two adolescent boys, brothers, helped a frail old woman—their grandmother, perhaps—to a pew. A young woman took the arm of a young man and began to cry on his shoulder; he guided her away from the crowd.

The voices awoke.

The echoes of the words, the tears, the shuffling footsteps, touched the high rafters. The congregation began to mill, to pace, to whisper and huddle again, though now without the brooding sense of panic.

Simon thought of what treatment he could give Ralph. Would it be safe to treat him while wearing gloves and a mask? Simon had no pain killers in his home office, only penicillin tablets. Could that prevent secondary infection? Could he help Ralph in any significant way even with the resources of a hospital?

Footsteps behind him, scuffing on the stone steps of the church.

He knew the tread.

Andrea was entering the church, looking haggard and winded.

He moved toward her as she stepped upon the threshold, to embrace her and kiss her and. . . .

She pulled away from him, bright horror in her eyes. *"No, Simon! You mustn't come closer!"*

Light of the foreign sun touched her hair, struck her eyes at an angle that, under the sun of their world, would have made them shimmer with an inner radiance like that of amber, but here created a muted glow, so very dull compared to what her eyes had held upon the Earth.

Andrea took a small step toward him.

The arched frame of the door eclipsed the alien light that touched her hair and eyes.

She cocked her head, turned her neck.

And slowly pulled away the scarf Simon had bought her when they had first courted to reveal the lumps of frozen quicksilver on the skin of her neck, skin he had kissed a few hours before.

A small scent of dead skin.

Andrea covered her neck, as if in shame.

Rage . . .

Grief . . .

Fear . . .

Simon did not allow them to come forth.

Too much was at stake. Such emotions could open a floodgate. Simon and his neighbors had more at stake than their own survival, more at stake than their own cause of resistance against their captors.

The salvation of billions rested on their shoulders.

Desperate, Simon looked into the eyes of his doomed wife and spoke softly to her, unwilling to hear too clearly the hollowness he knew his voice would carry.

"Just . . . just from being in the car with that boy? Just from breathing the same air?"

"Yes," she whispered. "Tell them not to go through the fog. It's safe here. The air is safe here."

Simon turned toward his neighbors.

"*Is* it?" he asked, then met her eyes.

"Mr. Cashman and I . . ." Andrea gave a small choke. "We'll go back. . . ." A tilt of her head toward the wall of fog down the street; a shadow of empty resignation in her eyes, ". . . to *them*."

"No," said Simon.

Choice.

That which defines the soul.

"We may need your help."

He turned again to his fellow stolen specimens. They were besieged by fear and hopelessness, muted in this sanctuary built of stone drawn from the soil of the world they called home. They would need to find a strength like the stone of this church, to not become the labor pool of beings whose bodies had been rewritten by the fleshy stone of their own world.

He looked back to Andrea.

"We *will* need your help."

Andrea clutched her scarf around her neck, as if blocking a chill wind.

"We can't help you, Simon. I'm not even sure you can help yourselves."

Choice.

That which defines a single soul.

Or the souls of billions.

Our flesh has been stolen. And for an instant, in bright death, before being reassembled, we had no choice. We had no souls. Now, the strength of choice—the strength of the soul—is ours, again. We cannot waste it.

"Perhaps not. But maybe we can help the others."

She gave a confused look.

"Back on Earth," he said.

Simon walked to the center of the church. His neighbors filed out of the aisle before him. Ralph, Rhea, Andrea, and Father Fontanna stood in the doorway, shadowy in the hazy light. Just then the high pitched whine their captors directed toward the control area reasserted itself, as if it were on a cycle in tune with some unnamable rhythm at the fringes of human senses. He blocked the sound from his awareness.

The Authority had said, "*As anyone who has listened to a great and demonic speaker will tell you, sound waves can reach and subjugate the most recalcitrant organism.*"

Yet speech could liberate, as well.

Speech could awaken the necessity to exercise *choice*.

Simon raised his voice.

"There is no escape," he said.

Something visible spread through the crowd. It was the amassed effect of small movements, the slight castings of eyes downward, the slight bowing of heads, the small act of holding prayer books and rosaries tighter.

"For *us*," he said. "Not for *us*."

He raised his right arm toward the church door.

"We need not suffer the same fate as Ralph Cashman. Not so long as we stay in our homes and never wander more than six blocks in any direction. But we will never go back to the world we were stolen from. Understand that. *Never.*"

No small movements or gestures, as before. Yet there was a tangible turning inward among them—like the silent act of grieving.

Simon brought down his arm.

In the brief silence, the alien whine intruded.

"It's a lonely feeling, isn't it?"

Invoking anger and righteous fury, he said, "But we won't be lonely very long! Soon, the Earth's entire population will be teleported to this place. We will live in labor camps. We will toil, and we will sweat, and we will die in controlled areas."

He reined in his anger.

"Some of us may become infected. Contagion can occur even when we breathe the same air in a confined space. But enough of us will survive to make their project feasible! Out of the whole world of us, *enough* will survive."

He paused.

"If *we* survive."

Simon's heart beat against his chest. Part of him did not want to face what he himself was saying.

He looked to the faces of his neighbors, his fellow captives.

"We are their guinea pigs. . . . But we're *human* guinea pigs! And that gives us some choice in this experiment! *Human* choice!"

He gathered the strength to say what he must say next.

To do what he must do next.

"We can *choose* not to make their enslavement of our Earth feasible. . . . We can *choose* to *not* escape infection. We can deliberately become . . . what they are."

Simon took a deep breath, felt his heart slow. His neighbors were quiet, their voices still. They had about them a look of resignation, of acceptance. A few had their eyes half closed. A few moved their mouths in silent prayer. A man Simon had never seen before furrowed his brow, gave a pained look, and crossed himself.

Simon spoke again.

"My wife is already infected. I am going to take her hand. Will someone take mine?"

Simon walked the aisle toward Andrea. Father Fontanna stood by her side. The Cashmans stood nearby.

He was calm, at peace with what he had to do.

He gave his hand to his wife.

"Help us, Andrea."

Andrea looked into Simon's eyes.

All of existence, all the madness of the universe and all the memories of the world upon which God had first placed them, all the weight and implication and fear and loss they carried. . . .

Became nothing.

Became less than shadow in brilliant light.

Andrea reached out her hand.

Simon took it.

And felt a profound peace in his heart that he realized he had searched for all his life.

Ralph, pain written deeply in his features, turned to Rhea.

Rhea took his hand.

And Ralph Cashman, who had sobbed before while carrying the cast of wretchedness, now looked as if he would weep in the face of beatitude, as if Rhea's touch had offered him a redemption that transcended his stricken body.

Slowly, Ralph turned toward Andrea.

And extended his free hand.

Ralph's wedding ring shone brightly amid the dull metal eruptions.

Andrea took it, still holding Simon's hand in her right.

Father Fontanna stepped toward them. Simon looked to him, looked to the people standing, staring, behind the Father.

The priest took Simon's free hand, clasping it in both of his, for a moment. Then he removed his left hand from Simon's while still holding on with his right.

Father Fontanna turned slightly and reached out his left hand toward those huddled in the church.

A stirring in the crowd. An old man in a yarmulke stepped forward, holding hands with his wife, who clasped her shawl tight at her neck.

The old man took Fontanna's hand, without letting go of his wife.

A young woman came forward, holding rosary beads.

The old man's wife let go her shawl and extended her hand to the young woman; Simon saw the dull blue of numbers pressed into the skin of the older woman's wrist, saw the rosary swinging, still clutched in the younger woman's hand.

The young woman extended her hand. . . .

And people stepped forward, in twos and threes, to clasp hands with one another, creating a chain of humanity extending from the Holms and the Cashmans. Here, the hand of a child, guided by the hand of her mother. Here, the hand of a strong man joined to the pale hand of an old woman. Hands of different skin tones, extending all around as the press of humanity joined near the church's threshold.

The light changed.

Simon glanced over the shoulder of his wife, who was crying softly.

Quiet shadow took the street.

Quiet shadow deepened, dulling the harsh and brutal light.

Night was coming.

They were turning away from the hot and greedy star of their captors.

In darkness dispelled by the softness of candlelight, under faces of still martyrs of stone and glass, Simon found tranquillity among his neighbors, free from the light of the false and ugly sun.

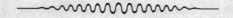

Church bells tolling.

Calling forth over the Sunday noon.

Calling forth faintly over the wound in the Earth where six square blocks had been stolen.

The wound is fenced off, much as a prison compound would be. Roads, streets, sidewalks, lead to a place that is now like a massive open grave. They are arteries of travel to a community that no longer exists.

At the edges of the pit, upon the severed roads and walkways, stand signs that read in bold letters of red and black:

DO NOT ENTER UPON OR CROSS THIS AREA. DO NOT TOUCH OR REMOVE POSSIBLY RADIOACTIVE DIRT OR ROCKS. IF YOU HAVE ANY KNOWLEDGE CONCERNING THIS DISAPPEARANCE, PLEASE CONTACT YOUR LOCAL POLICE DEPARTMENT.

The signs stand, silent as grave stones, mute testimonials to people twice martyred.

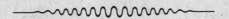

MICHAEL MARANO is a horror writer and an aficionado of old TV and movies. As "Mad Professor Mike," he reviews horror movies on Movie Magazine, *a public radio show. His first novel,* Dawn Song, *will be published by Tor Books in 1997.*

"The Message" came from another world—or from the inside of Jennifer's head. She was sure she could tell the difference, and her husband was equally sure she was wrong. When your only ally is a hospital janitor with a record of mental illness, how sure can you be?

The Message

Adaptation by Richard A. Lupoff
Original screenplay by Brad Wright

Hospitals have a sound all their own. Whispered conversations. Urgent announcements blaring from loudspeakers. The sounds of laughter and love when good news arrives. The sobs of grief when the news is bad.

Jennifer Winter heard none of this. She sat patiently, waiting for—something. Her hair was dark and sleek, her face was smooth and as filled with character as it was with beauty. Her keen blue eyes darted here and there until her attention was caught by a small boy seated in another of the hospital's inhospitable plastic chairs.

A smile animated Jennifer's features. She raised graceful hands and gestured silently: a fleeting, graceful ballet in which the dancers were ten strong, lithe fingers.

The boy returned Jennifer's smile. It was as if her friendly interest were contagious. He waved a greeting. His lips moved. He was talking to her. She concentrated on his lips; for a moment she was unsure of his message, then followed the direction of his gesture.

She turned to see a massive form looming over her: a man in workman's clothes, a mop held in his oversized hands. His hair was cropped short and a small beard and mustache rounded out his fleshy, creased face. He had the look of a man battered by life. He'd been talking for some time, but now Jennifer read his words. "Excuse me, miss?"

She followed his gaze to the floor. A recent stain cried out for attention, and he was there to attend to it. Jennifer moved her feet out of the way and he swiped at the stain until it disappeared.

"Sorry," she said. She spoke with clarity but with the distinctive accent of one who had never heard human speech, had learned to speak not by imitation but by painful struggle, by endless commitment to trial and error until she could approximate the speech that comes effortlessly to the hearing.

The hulking janitor held the mop handle beneath one arm and signed back.

Jennifer smiled. It was obvious that the man was struggling to learn to sign; his gestures were like baby-talk. She said, "That's okay," and he smiled back and moved on. He seemed pathetically grateful for the smallest show of kindness.

Even the humblest of honest labor. . . .

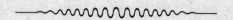

While Jennifer waited, two men studied an MRI of her skull. One was her husband. His face was handsome but drawn with concern. His hair was thick, a rich, wavy brown, but he ran his fingers through it nervously. He was having a hard time understanding what he saw.

The second man was Jennifer's physician, Alex Madison. He could have posed for an ad in some medical trade journal, almost the parody of the mature, concerned practitioner. His hair was silvery-gray; he wore glasses rimmed in the same color, and fluorescent lights gleamed off their lenses. He pleaded with Jennifer's husband, hoping to make him understand his findings. His voice indicated that this was far from their first dialogue.

"That's the implant, Mr. Winter. It's right where it belongs, that little square you can see in her inner ear. It's at the cochlea, right where we wanted it. The nerve endings should be doing their work now, and they're not."

"But why not? You said you were confident—"

"I was wrong."

"Well, take another look at the image. There has to be some explanation."

Madison pointed at the dark square in the picture. "It's right where it belongs. It should be working. I thought it would work. Hell, Sam, I helped *invent* the damned thing. But the nerves aren't connected the way we hoped and she isn't hearing. We have to go out and tell her. You may think it's kinder to withhold the information, but it isn't. Not really."

He started for the doorway but Sam stopped him with a hand on his elbow. "You say it doesn't work. Then how can she be starting to hear things?"

Madison shook his head. "She can't." A moment fled silently. Then he added, "It's impossible."

"My wife says she's hearing sounds." Sam sounded angry now.

"But she's never *heard* sound. Maybe she's just misinterpreting another sensation."

Sam shook his head.

"Or maybe the hope of hearing has created a sort of—auditory hallucination. I have no idea. I'm out of my league in that department. If you'd like I can arrange a meeting with Dr. Leiberman."

Sam shook his head, refusing to accept the idea. Then, gradually, he seemed to come around. "If Jen wants to talk with a psychiatrist, I'll call a psychiatrist." For a moment he held his breath. Then he exhaled, and it was as if half the air had been released from a bulging balloon.

"She was so sure," he said. "So. . . . It's going to break her heart."

———∿∿∿∿∿∿∿∿———

The boy stood when the woman who was obviously his mother reached to take his hand. Their appointment was here and he gave Jennifer Winter one more small smile as he left the waiting area.

Jennifer glanced at the hulking janitor, then impatiently at her watch. Sam had gone ahead to discuss her MRI with Dr. Madison. She hadn't wanted to face the physician. Not today. She was too upset, her disagreement with her husband had been too intense. Let him confront the specialist; he would report back to her and she would decide what step to take next.

Ten minutes after three.

Jennifer blinked. She heard something. No matter how skeptical Sam and Dr. Madison were, she *knew* that she was hearing. She inhaled sharply, touched her ear, stared at the hulking janitor.

"What do you want?" she asked him. She was careful to enunciate. Unable to hear herself speak, she controlled every consonant, modulated every vowel precisely.

The janitor turned. There was a confused air about him. He said, "Hm? I didn't say anything."

Now Jennifer mirrored his confusion. The man smiled at her, turned away and started back to his menial task, but Jennifer pursued their primitive conversation. "I heard you," she insisted. "You asked for help."

The janitor shook his head, no. "I didn't say anything."

The dialogue was interrupted by the arrival of Sam Winters and Alex Madison. Husband and doctor.

Jennifer turned away from the janitor to face the two men, confusion and anxiety written plain in her features.

"Jen, what is it?" Sam could sign, not as well as his wife but better than the shambling janitor.

Jennifer signed urgently. Sometimes she accompanied her signing with spoken words; with Sam, she knew that was unnecessary. He could read her hands.

She told him that the big janitor had asked her for help. He had asked, and she had heard him.

"Did you?" he asked the janitor. "Did you ask my wife to help you?"

The man shrugged. Despite his massive size he seemed terrified of offending, as if he had been abused at some point and had never fully recovered from the mistreatment. He stammered, "No, I was just, uh, just cleaning the floor, and—"

Alex Madison, as much an authority figure in his white coat as a general in dress uniform would have been, interrupted. "It's all right," he told the janitor, "you don't have to worry about it."

The big man nodded and turned away, carefully mopping the hospital floor, as if he was relieved to escape from these threatening people and return to the safety of his little, undemanding job.

Madison stood facing Jennifer, making certain she could read his lips. "We've just gone over the results of the tests we ran."

Jennifer signed her response and spoke as well. "What is it?"

"I know you had high hopes." Madison was a disappointment man himself. "But the implant still isn't working. There's no change from—"

Jennifer's eyes widened. She looked around, looked up at the brightly lit hospital corridor ceiling, looking for the source of—something. Amazed, Sam Winter and Alex Madison stood blinking at each other.

In a clear voice, Jennifer said, "Yes, I hear you."

"Jennifer? Who are you talking to?" Sam demanded.

"I don't know." She looked around, puzzlement in her eyes. "Someone who needs my help."

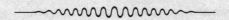

Jennifer opened the door of the apartment she and Sam called home. She brushed past the baby-sitter and went down the hallway.

Sam arrived home just seconds later. He looked harried and upset. The baby-sitter reached for her coat. "Little Allison was an angel all day," she managed, "she's fast asleep. Mr. Winter—I hope Jennifer's all right."

Sam turned as if he hadn't noticed her before. "She will be," he managed, "thanks again for coming, Mrs. Henderson, it's really great having you in the building."

The sitter departed. They could settle up for her hours another time. Besides, she loved little Allison and at her age she didn't have much else to do with her days. She'd said so herself, said that she'd sit with Allison for the sheer pleasure of it, even if they didn't pay her.

Sam followed Jennifer down the hallway and into their bedroom. When he walked in she was sitting on the edge of their bed, her head held in her hands. Sam crouched in front of her. He had to talk with her, and she had to see either his lips or his hands; she would not hear his words.

"Jen, I'm sorry. I was hoping for good news too. Madison was so confident, he seemed so sure he knew what he was doing. . . ."

Jennifer signed her reply. The dance of her hands was a dance of anger and confusion and misery. *I hear. I know I hear, and no one believes me.*

"I want to believe you, Jen. But we've done tests. Controlled tests, and—nothing. So—I just don't understand—what is it that you're hearing? Can you hear me now?"

Miserably, Jennifer lowered her head. She spoke aloud and clearly, a single word. "No."

Sam took her hands in his. He looked into her face so she could see his lips. "Honey, I know how much you wanted to hear Allison's first words. I know how much you wanted to be able to hear her cry."

"The most beautiful music there is," she said. And tears glistened on her own cheeks. "My father used to tell me that. The sound of your baby crying is the most beautiful sound there is. I want to hear my baby."

"Maybe your imagination is turning that desire into something." Sam tilted his head, trying to read his answer in her face.

Jennifer shook her head. She withdrew her hands from Sam's and signed her reply.

Sam nodded comprehension. Then he said, "But I don't understand how it's a *real* sound. Dr. Madison says that's impossible."

Aloud, Jennifer said, "It's the difference—" Then she continued in sign, weaving words between them in the air. And aloud, Sam echoed her signs, "—between actually seeing me—my face—in the light of day, and imagining it in the dark."

She took his hand, suddenly afraid. And in return he took hers, and kissed it tenderly. If love could overcome cold reality, she would have heard the symphony of nature, the beating of his heart. But she did not hear, and that she believed she did worried him more than her deafness itself.

"It was stronger today than it was yesterday, wasn't it?" he asked her. "This—this sense that you're hearing?"

Jennifer nodded. Yes.

"Then we'll see what happens. Doctors have been wrong before. Madison could be wrong. If you're hearing, then who cares what they say?"

When she didn't respond he tried once more. "Right, Jen?"

She smiled and touched his face. If he believed her, if he believed *in* her. . . .

─────~~~∿∿∿∿∿∿∿~~~─────

Allison lay in her crib, in her own room, while Jennifer and Sam lay in their bed. Sam's eyes were closed, his breathing was steady and peaceful. Not so, Jennifer.

Her eyes popped open. The world could say what it would, *she was hearing something!* She threw back the coverlet and sat bolt upright. She turned her head, trying to locate the source of the sound.

She reached for her husband, grasped his arm, waking him.

"Jen, what is it?"

The bedroom was darkened but there was enough light to see her face, to read lips. She said, "The baby's crying."

Sam tilted his head. "She is?"

Jennifer climbed out of the bed and hurried from the room. Sitting in bed, Sam said, "I don't hear anything, Jen. She's—" That was getting him nowhere. He climbed out of bed and followed her toward Allison's nursery.

Jennifer stood over their daughter's crib. She leaned over the child, tenderly lifted her in her arms and held her against her shoulder. She rocked gently back and forth, as she would to comfort a crying child.

But this child was not crying. She was not crying at all.

Sam stood in the doorway. The hall light behind him set his figure in silhouette, his shadow crossing the carpet like the outline of a fallen giant. Startled, Jennifer turned. Now that she saw him, there was enough light for her to see his lips and his hands, should he choose to speak or to sign to her. He did both.

"Jennifer, she's sound asleep. Just let her sleep."

She patted the baby's back gently, as if she were crying, as if she were soothing her.

"Jen, put her down. She wasn't crying, Jen."

Jennifer held the baby away so she could look into her face. Her eyes were closed. Her breathing was soft; Jennifer could see the baby's chest rising and falling, gently, steadily. She spread her fingers across the tiny chest and felt its steady rise and fall. She returned to the crib and leaned over it with Allison in her arms and carefully laid the baby in her crib. She pulled a light blanket over her, more for comfort than for warmth.

Sam put his arm around Jennifer's shoulders and walked her gently from the nursery.

They didn't return to bed. Instead Sam led her into the living room where she sat in a big overstuffed chair. She pulled her legs up under her and sat there in the semidarkness. She could still see her husband, still see what he had to say to her. She smiled at him.

He said, "You okay, hon?"

Jennifer's hands told him that she was all right, she just needed a little time to herself.

"Okay," he nodded. "Do you . . ." He stifled a yawn. "Do you want me to sit up with you?"

Jennifer shook her head. She managed a smile. It was intended to be reassuring, but it was obviously artificial, forced.

Sam blinked. He was keeping up with his work, or trying to, at the same time that he was trying to see Jennifer through a growing crisis. So far he'd been able to hold the line. He wasn't a big dome, high-tech wizard. He was a salesman, a solid, old-fashioned professional. He was good at his work, and proud of providing a comfortable, secure home for his family. But he wondered how long he could go on burning the candle at both ends before his work began to suffer.

He said, "I've got to get up in a few hours, so. . . ." He switched to signing. Somehow the silent communion of signing brought him closer to Jennifer than spoken words could ever do. His signing did not have the fluid grace of Jen's, but he was fast and clear. He signed, "Goodnight," and dropped his hands and headed for the bedroom.

With Sam's departure, Jennifer was able to drop her strained smile. She squeezed her eyes shut and pressed her fingertips to her forehead. She didn't know if she was going to weep, didn't know if she wanted to weep, even if she *could* weep.

In time she returned to bed and lay beside her husband and managed, at last, to doze off.

Did she dream? Or was it real? Did a strong breeze lift the sheer draperies that hung before the windows, and sweep a wisp of cloth across Jennifer's face?

She wakened and swung her feet over the edge of the bed. Unconsciously she smoothed the silvery material of her nightgown. Was it morning already? Why was the bedroom so preternaturally bright?

She edged closer to the window and blinked at what she saw.

The sun—was it the sun?—was huge. No glowing disk in one corner of the sky, it *filled* the sky. It was clearly three-dimensional. Sunspots and solar storms crawled across its face like grubs on the skin of an apple.

Another gust swept the sheer draperies over her, like the grasping hands of a giant.

She averted her eyes from the swollen, turgid, glowing globe. She felt beads of sweat bursting from her forehead, as if the sun were blasting her with a heat greater than that of the hottest summer's day.

She wondered for a moment if the earth had been suddenly, catastrophically, ripped from its orbit and flung toward the sun. Closer and closer it would approach, until all life was exterminated on the planet, and then the hot, parched globe would fall into the sun itself.

Somewhere a clock clicked to 3:10 A.M. and Jennifer uttered a despairing gasp. She held her head in both hands, staring at the darkened living room. She had fallen asleep in the easy chair. It had been a dream. It had.

But it had seemed so real. As if she had lived through another being, seen through another's eyes, felt the roasting heat of the sun with another's skin.

Shaken, she managed to stumble back to the bedroom, this time digging her fingernails into the palms of her hands to make sure that she was awake, that she was really experiencing the truth of the moment. She climbed into bed beside her husband but she could not sleep. She stared at the ceiling, struggling to comprehend what was happening to her.

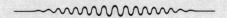

The next day Jennifer sat cross-legged in front of a classroom full of seven year olds. Every child in the room was hearing-impaired. She smiled at them, feeling the love flow from herself to them, feeling the well of love replenished ever more generously as it was dispensed.

This was a special part of Jennifer's life. As much as she loved Sam, as much as she loved Allison, their hearing and her own deafness comprised a barrier between them. With these children, there was no such barrier.

It was story time, and they were telling each other a familiar fairy tale. The children knew the story as well as Jennifer did; its very familiarity made it useful as they learned to sign and to read signing.

Little pig, little pig, let me come in! her graceful hands danced.

Not by the hair of my chinny-chin-chin! a room full of children responded silently.

Then I'll huff and I'll puff and I'll blow your house down! the wolf threatened, using Jennifer's fingers to make his menacing words.

And all the children became the wolf, and blew, and from somewhere Jennifer produced a fluffy dandelion and joined them in blowing. The dandelion seeds floated like feathers scattering from a broken pillow, or like spaceships fleeing from a dying world. They filled the air with tiny specks of dancing, drifting whiteness.

One dandelion seed drifted by Jennifer. She managed to catch it, a tiny, almost insubstantial thing. She studied it, wondering.

Wondering.

But then story time was over, and the school day was nearly finished. Jennifer walked to the blackboard. Above it a big old circular school clock read 3:09. Jennifer lifted an eraser and swept the blackboard clean of the writing and drawing that had accumulated through the day.

She picked up a piece of chalk. At the top of the board she wrote in large, strong letters, HOMEWORK FOR TONIGHT.

She looked over her shoulder to see that her charges had opened their notebooks, prepared to write down the assignment. She turned back to the blackboard and wrote, READ CHAPTER 11.

The big clock clicked over to 3:10.

Something lanced through Jennifer's brain with an agonizing intensity. It was a sound. Whether Dr. Madison's implant had kicked in at last or this was some other phenomenon in action, she had no idea, but Jennifer knew beyond question that she was *hearing*.

And she was writing. Her hand moved furiously, as if with a will of its own, writing furiously, relentlessly.

The seven year olds were frightened. They had never seen their teacher act like this before, and what's more, they had never seen writing like this either.

Jennifer continued, line after line. When she reached the end of the blackboard she moved to the next line, like the typing element on an old-style typewriter sliding on its cable to the far end of the carriage. Without pausing to think, she wrote, and wrote, and wrote.

Finally one child, perhaps more concerned than the others, perhaps more courageous, rose from her place and crossed to her teacher. She tugged at Jennifer's free hand while the other hand continued to write. Jennifer paid no attention. More alarmed than ever, the seven year old ran from the room. She had to find someone to help!

She scurried past a school custodian, through familiar corridors, until she reached the principal's office. She pounded on the door, then let herself in, confronting a florid-faced man wearing a gray suit. He sat at a cluttered desk but looked up, startled, when she clattered across the room and seized his hand.

He didn't know what was wrong, but he recognized one of Jennifer Winter's hearing-impaired students, and he ran with her back to Jennifer's classroom.

Standing in the doorway, he saw Jennifer still writing as fast as she could, her hand working like a mechanical instrument, pounding out the digits on the blackboard. She was surrounded by her students, wonderstruck by what they were seeing. Only three characters, repeated endlessly and in endlessly varied combinations:

0010X000 10X01 10XX01 111001 1X010
110001X 00001 0101 01 0010X000 10X01

Jennifer wrote and wrote, as fast as her hand would move. Unaware of her classroom, unaware of the children she loved, she wrote and wrote and wrote until. . . .

She felt a hand grasp hers and stop her from writing. She turned and looked into the face of the principal, a man she had known and respected for years. As she read the concern and puzzlement in his face, he read the bafflement and despair in hers.

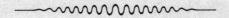

Sam Winter thanked his lucky stars for the neighbor who was willing to stay with Allison whenever they needed her. He'd learned of the bizarre incident in Jennifer's classroom and had rushed to the hospital where the principal had brought her.

Jennifer had calmed down to a certain extent, and seemed willing to sit in the waiting room while Sam talked with the doctors, out of eyesight and out of what would have been earshot for a hearing person. She'd insisted only on bringing a notepad with her, and a pencil, and she wrote and wrote, passively accepting her surroundings as long as she was permitted to write and write and write.

Only the vibration of a mechanical floor polisher broke her concentration. She clutched her pad and pencil but she looked up from her work and recognized the hulking janitor she had seen at the hospital before.

The janitor smiled shyly at Jennifer, released the handles of the polishing machine and clicked off the power. He raised his hands to the level of his chest and carefully, diligently signed a full sentence, mouthing the words at the same time. "It's very nice to see you again today." He waited for a response.

Jennifer stared. After a long moment she turned back to her pad and resumed writing.

The janitor leaned over, worry written on his oversized features. He worked hard, trying to sign clearly at the same time that he spoke aloud. "Did I say something wrong?"

Jennifer looked up. The janitor couldn't tell whether she had read his signing but at least she seemed aware of his presence.

"I was just saying it was nice to see you again," he repeated. "I remember you from the last time you were here." He paused, waiting for a reply, but none came so he resumed. "I'm just learning how to sign, because of Dr. Madison working here. We get a lot of deaf patients in this wing because of Dr. Madison's work. So I hope I didn't offend—"

Jennifer cut him off with a gesture, indicating her notepad, mimicking the message that she was too busy writing to stop and chat.

The janitor didn't give up. "What are you writing?"

She signed back, "I don't know."

"You don't know?" he echoed. "Or you don't want *me* to know?"

This time the message got through. Jennifer gestured toward herself, indicating that *she* didn't know what she was writing. But whatever it was, she was committed to it. She was not about to stop writing her zeroes and her ones and her letters.

But the letters were all the same. Every one was an *X*.

The janitor shrugged. Clearly she didn't want to talk with him. But his curiosity remained unassuaged. He clicked the floor polisher back to life and maneuvered it around the waiting room. When he passed by

Jennifer he moved the heavy machine close to her chair so she had to lift her feet from the floor. Driven by curiosity, he leaned over to get a look at the mysterious notebook.

Jennifer looked up, clearly irritated by the janitor's annoying persistence.

Like a child caught spying on his parents, the hulking man said, "I'm sorry. I'm. . . . It's just that it looked like binary, and I thought maybe you were a computer programmer."

This time he had spoken aloud, and he was sure that she had read his lips, but when she asked him to repeat he was able to sign the key words. *Binary code. Machine language.*

Jennifer lifted her pad. "This?"

Now the janitor got a closer look at her page. "Yes. It looks like binary, all right, except—I don't know what the X's mean."

Jennifer asked, "How do you know?" He took on new importance to her. He was just a janitor. Hundreds of people must see him at work every day, and never even notice. Like countless other workers, he blended into the background of everyday life.

"Oh, I—" He paused. The look on his face suggested that he was dealing with a painful recollection. "I used to work with computers. That was in my old job."

Urgently, she demanded, "What does it say, can you tell me?"

The big janitor made a helpless gesture. "I'm not saying I know what it *says*. Binary isn't exactly a language you can read. I'm just guessing at this. I'd have to input it into my computer at home and see what comes out."

This was strange. This shy, self-effacing, menial working man—was he a computer scientist in his spare time? He'd used computers in his old job, he said. It didn't make much sense.

Still . . . Jennifer held up her notepad and tore off a handful of pages. She thrust them at the hulking man. She nodded and gestured. There was no doubt about her meaning. He was to take the pages and do exactly as he'd said: Input them into his computer and see what came back out.

Reluctantly, he accepted the pages. "It could take a really long time," he told her. The expression on her face showed determination. "Okay," he relented, "sure, I guess I could. Um, I just," he hesitated, then asked, "How did you write all this down if you don't know what it is?"

Jennifer shrugged. She just didn't know.

More baffled than ever, the janitor stood over the seated woman, the notebook pages in his hand. Then he turned, jolted from his puzzlement, by the arrival of her husband. And he was angry.

Angry and worried.

But mainly angry.

He rushed past the janitor, to his wife's side. Then, almost as an afterthought, to the other man, "Do you mind?"

No way was the janitor going to quarrel with Sam Winter. He backed away and returned to his floor polisher. But he waved the notebook pages so that

Jennifer Winter could see them but Sam could not. The message from him to the woman was clear. He would keep his promise.

Jennifer Winter was the center of this whirlwind, and once she recognized what had happened she began signing rapidly to her husband. But Sam interrupted:

"I know all about what happened. Your principal called and—and why the hell didn't they take you directly to our family doctor?"

Jennifer's response was a single short sentence that spoke volumes. "Something's happening to me."

Sam squeezed his eyes shut. How right she was, and how terribly afraid he was of what seemed to be happening! He held her tight.

———~~~~~~~~~———

There was no way out of it. If Jennifer hadn't consented to see the psychiatrist, Sam might have had to give consent for her, and then her fate would have been taken out of her hands. As things were, at least she was here voluntarily and she controlled her own destiny.

At least for now.

Dr. Leiberman must have gone out of his way to make his office non-threatening, and to develop a manner that projected friendly concern and sympathy. His salt-and-pepper hair was curly and slightly unkempt, and he wore a soft polo shirt, not a white coat, to work. He'd seen too many cases and heard too many stories of patients' blood pressure zooming, their pulse-rates racing, a whole array of symptoms appearing just from a visit to the doctor. He'd even heard of seemingly healthy patients dying in their doctors' offices. Those stories might be apocryphal, but still and all. . . .

It was called the white-coat syndrome, and he did everything he could to avoid it.

It didn't take away the fact that he was a psychiatrist, a head-shrinker, and that Jennifer was there because her husband thought she was hearing voices and that those voices were imaginary, and if that didn't mean that at least one of them was crazy it would have to do until the real thing came along.

Sam was right, Jennifer was hearing voices. But they were not imaginary, she was certain they were not imaginary. And while she was upset—very upset, dreadfully upset—she was definitely not crazy.

It was unfortunate that Leiberman did not know signing. Jennifer might have relied on lip-reading and spoken so he could understand, but Sam had volunteered to stand by and help with the translation, and that made things easier for all concerned.

They started with small talk and medical history, and Leiberman had frowned and harrumphed and jotted lengthy notes when they came to the part about Alex Madison's little circuit chip and the procedure in which he had implanted it in her inner ear. If Madison hadn't sent over a case history that verified the implant story, Leiberman would have doubted it to start with. But that was all preliminary, Jennifer knew it was all preliminary.

"Those voices, Jennifer . . . Are they asking you to do anything you don't want to do?"

There it was. This was the beginning of the main event.

Jennifer shook her head, no.

"Good." Leiberman smiled reassuringly. "What do they want you to do, then?"

Jennifer only shrugged. Her husband volunteered an answer for her. "She says it's a sound she can actually hear in her head." Before he could go any farther, Jennifer shot him a look whose meaning was more than clear. She did not want him to furnish answers for her. She would tell Leiberman what she wanted him to know.

"You're right," Sam apologized, "I'm sorry. You go ahead, I'll just help with the translation."

"When I'm awake," she resumed, "I hear voices I don't understand. I can write out what they're saying but I don't know the meaning. I can just sense that they want help. *My* help."

"But you *did* think you heard the baby crying, Jen," Sam put in.

She shook her head. She was not to be sidetracked. She resumed her story in sign, her fingers flying so rapidly that Sam could barely keep up as he translated her signs into spoken words.

"But when I fall asleep—I have trouble sleeping, but when I manage to fall asleep—I have dreams. Dreams of the sun. The sun is so hot, so big in the sky. And I'm traveling. I don't know if it's the whole earth or it's just me, but I'm racing toward the sun and it's getting hotter and hotter and brighter and brighter. . . ."

Ever calm, Leiberman jotted a note. Then he asked, "Do you hear these voices now?"

Jennifer nodded. There was nothing hesitant or ambiguous about the gesture.

Sam, watching his wife, let out a concerned sigh.

Jennifer held out her hands and Leiberman understood her request. He turned a page on his notepad so she could start with a fresh sheet of paper, and handed her the pad and a pen. She began writing furiously, her hand racing across the page, line after line after line.

Watching Jennifer with concern, Leiberman looked up and exchanged nods with Sam. He reached for his pad, patiently waiting for Jennifer to finish a line, then accepted the pad and paper when she released them. He looked at what Jennifer had written, never indicating pleasure or dismay, satisfaction or surprise, at what she had written there.

Leiberman turned his face back toward Jennifer and spoke clearly to make sure she could follow his every word. "I don't understand this, Jennifer. What does it mean? How does this indicate that the voices want help? I can't read this writing."

She shrugged, then spoke to her husband in sign. Without translating for Leiberman, Sam asked, "Who, Jen?"

"Sam, please. . . ."

Sam yielded. "Doctor, she said she just met a man who understands it and is going to translate it for her."

Leiberman said, "Good, good, then we'll know." But did he believe in this "man," or did he believe he was just part of Jennifer's delusion? "Does it hurt you to hear these voices?" he asked.

"It hurts not to. It hurts when I try to block them out, or when I stop writing."

Leiberman pursed his lips. He handed her pen and paper again. Even as he continued to ask her questions, even as she tried to pay attention to his questions and to answer them, she found herself becoming absorbed in her task.

Writing, writing, writing.

Ones and zeroes and X's.

"I can't tell you what this is about, Jennifer," Leiberman said. "I know you have terribly troubling questions, and I can't give you the answers. But I think I can give you something to ease that pain while we look for the answers together."

When she didn't respond to the suggestion, he tapped her gently on the shoulder to get her to look at him, and tried a more direct approach. "Would that be a good place to start?"

She nodded absently, as if she'd been listening to him with a small part of her mind, and heard what he said, and found it not disagreeable. But she was busy, busy, busy. She did not look up from the pad to see the look that was exchanged between her husband and her psychiatrist. She hardly even noticed when the two of them slipped from the room, leaving her with the pad and pen, leaving her to write, and to write, and to write.

Outside, in the relative privacy of the corridor, Leiberman spoke first. "I think it's fairly likely that Jennifer's had what we call a first break psychotic episode."

Sam Winter shook his head. "She thought—*we* thought—that the cochlea implant she got had just started to work for some reason. Madison put it in almost a year ago. It didn't do any good, but it didn't seem to do any harm so we just left it. We didn't want to put Jennifer through another procedure. But then she started hearing voices, and we thought it was working after all, but Madison insists that's impossible. So, this—" He halted, out of what to say.

"It's nothing to be ashamed of," Leiberman said. "Sam, I'd like to start her on a mild antipsychotic, a drug I've had a lot of success with."

Sam was aghast. "Oh, God."

"I know that you think this couldn't possibly just *happen* to your wife, Sam. But believe me. . . . Voices, writing gibberish, this mystery man who is going to translate that nonsense-scribbling and tell her what it means. . . ." He shook his head sadly. "It's all characteristic of a first break schizophrenic episode."

Sam raised his hands as if he could physically turn away the bad news. "We've got a six-month-old baby at home, and it's not like she didn't already have a disability. . . ."

"Don't worry," Leiberman tried to reassure him. "As soon as you're home and Jennifer's on her medication, everything will get back to normal. We're not talking about doping her up with massive amounts of drugs. This will help her calm down, and if we're lucky it will make the voices go away."

Sam shook his head. "It sounds too good to be true. You can just make the voices stop, make her—" he swallowed, reluctant to use the word, but managed to resume "—make her hallucinations disappear?"

Leiberman tilted his head. "Not quite that good. What these antipsychotics do is just damp down the neural activity a little. These voices and such, we think they come from misfiring neurons. Random signals that get interpreted as words. We can put a damper on that activity and the people get a lot better, but they sometimes report a general sense of, well, mental sloth."

Sam looked worried.

"It isn't perfect," Leiberman said, "but it's a small price to pay, believe me."

Sam tried to believe him.

Living in an otherwise-vacant warehouse might not quite have met the zoning regulations, but the big janitor's landlord was happy to take in even a little rent, and his tenant was happy to get far more space than he could have afforded on a janitor's salary, if he'd lived in a better residential neighborhood.

Nobody blew the whistle. Everybody was happy.

He'd made a cozy living room for himself, a functional kitchen, and a work area that would have had a science fiction fan of fifty years before drooling with envy. On one side of the room, on top of a battered wooden desk, stood a computer system that would have made a nerdish salesman with a plastic protector on his pocket and inch-thick glasses slipping down his nose start to babble about "top of the line" and "state of the art."

On the other side of the room, its carefully capped lens pointed at a large undraped window, stood a lovingly-cared-for and expensive looking telescope.

Home from the hospital, the big man changed from diffident janitor to data entry clerk. He booted up the computer, spread the deaf woman's notebook pages on the scarred mahogany desktop, and prepared to start entering zeroes and ones and X's. He stretched, took a deep breath, and plunged into his task.

It was going to be a long night.

———~~~~~~~~~———

In Jennifer and Sam's apartment, little Allison slept peacefully in her crib while her parents lay side by side in their bed. Jennifer felt the rhythm of her husband's steady breathing. In a way she envied him, but in another way . . . she had entered into some new adventure, almost into a new life. She knew this even though she did not know what the adventure could mean or what that new life could be.

At last she managed to drift off into a light doze, but almost at once, even without wakening, she winced. Her head rolled from side to side. She kept her eyes shut, squeezing them and clenching her jaw, but it was as if a voice were coming toward her, coming closer and growing louder and—

She jumped out of bed. The clock on the nightstand read 3:09. Beside it, the light on the monitor connected to Allison's room glowed steadily. The monitor was useless to Jennifer, but Sam would hear any disturbance from the baby's room. Guided by something unidentifiable, Jennifer ran to the window and looked out at the night sky.

The canopy of stars was inexplicably clear and bright and ineffably beautiful. Then, on the horizon, a bright light began to glow. It was the sun, rising in the small hours of the night. It was huge, even huger and far more intense than it had been when she saw it before. Many times the size it should be, searingly hot and blindingly bright.

But the rest of the sky remained as black as ever. The stars remained bright and sharp, but they were moving, moving as if she were seeing them from the observation deck of some incredible speeding spaceship.

How fast would a ship have to move, for the distant stars to shift visibly from their places?

Jennifer opened her arms wide, as if she were a maiden about to be sacrificed by some pagan cult, a virgin taking the sun itself as her lover and her god.

Behind her, as far from her thoughts as the deepest tomb of the first Pharaoh, her husband slept. And the bedside clock clicked over to 3:10.

Waves of sensation and of information swept through her mind, obliterating all thought and all consciousness. Her sense of time vanished; she could not tell whether the experience flashed by in a fraction of a second or stretched through an unmeasurable eternity. But suddenly it was over and she looked out the window at the normal night sky. She lowered her eyes and saw the city's skyline, a jagged silhouette against the ghostly light of the heavens.

She felt a touch and turned.

It was Sam, out of bed and standing beside her and holding her now. She was back on earth, back in her home, her reality, back in her husband's arms. She wanted to tell him something but she didn't want to speak aloud. She wanted the silent intimacy of signing.

Gently she freed her hands and faced Sam and signed in the dim light of their bedroom. *The voices have stopped.*

Sam blinked. He spoke to her and there was enough light in the room that she could read his lips. "Stopped? Just like that?"

All she did was smile, and he read that smile and embraced her. He said, "That's such a relief."

Then the speaker in the monitor came to life. Something had awakened Allison, and she had begun to cry. Sam released Jennifer and headed for the nursery. Jennifer started after him but he stopped her. "You go back to bed. You must be exhausted."

Jennifer shook her head. Despite her deafness, she was able to voice her determination. "I want to!"

Sam acceded. He watched Jennifer hurry toward the baby's nursery. He worried. His wife had been through ups and downs, hopes raised and dashed.

She had experienced a frightening series of auditory hallucinations. What lay ahead for her and for him and for their child?

At breakfast Sam and Jennifer faced each other in the sunlit kitchen, across the homely array of boiled eggs and toast, orange juice and hot tea. Allison had been cleaned and fed and was playing contentedly in her crib. This was the life they had hoped for, for so long.

"Kind of nice, isn't it?" Sam asked.

Jennifer read his lips, signed back, *Won't they miss you at work?*

Sam pursed his lips. "Absolutely. They're probably just standing around right now, wondering if the company will collapse because their star sales rep missed a day." He grew serious. He said, "I want to be here with you, to help you through this thing, Jen."

You think I'm crazy, she signed.

"No! I don't." He picked up his cup and looked into it, then lowered it again without drinking. "Do *you* think you're crazy?"

Jennifer shook her head, then signed her answer. Almost as if he were unable to understand, Sam repeated back to her. "You had the dream again? The dream of the giant sun?"

She nodded and he made the mistake of trying to get her to abandon her belief. "You know," he smiled, "Dr. Leiberman could be right."

Her look told him what that suggestion was worth.

"I'm sorry," he managed. "I was trying to be—never mind. I'm just sorry." He studied her face. Her expression told him what his apology was worth.

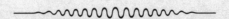

In his warehouse-apartment, the giant, shambling janitor had labored to enter those pages of ones and zeroes and X's into his computer. He'd studied the deaf woman's writing and tried scanning the material into the computer, but her handwriting didn't have the machine-like regularity that the scanning software could process accurately. Maybe someday, maybe when the system was more evolved, but for now the task meant nothing but endless hours at the keyboard, until his eyes were ready to fall from his head and his shoulders felt as if someone had driven an ice pick between them.

But the job was done.

To the big man's surprise, the computer's printer started humming and a sheet of paper emerged. Then another, and another, and another. Without disturbing the sequence of the pages, he removed the first few sheets from the printer's output tray and spread them on top of a battered work-table.

He leaned over the sheets, then straightened so he could take them all in at once. He squinted as if he couldn't believe his eyes, he shook his head, grinned in amazement and delight, and whispered the only words he could think of, "Ohhh, my goodness!"

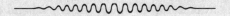

Jennifer stood in the doorway of the apartment, dressed for her next appointment with Dr. Leiberman. Sam stood watching her, their baby in his arms. "You're sure you want to go on your own," he asked Jennifer, "you sure you don't want me to come with you?"

Shaking her head, Jennifer managed a smile. Then she signed, *I want to go alone. Allison needs some quality time with her daddy.*

"We could take her with us," Sam persisted. "Little Ally has fond memories of the hospital. She had such a great time being born."

Aloud, Jennifer told him, "I'll be fine."

"I know you'll be fine. I just thought—" By the time he'd got that far, Sam realized that he was not going to change Jennifer's mind. Instead, he changed his tack. "Whatever. It's up to you. Me 'n Ally can watch the soaps."

Jennifer smiled at her husband and blew a kiss to her daughter and pulled the door shut behind herself.

When she reached the hospital she was told by an efficient nurse that Dr. Leiberman was running a little late and would she please make herself comfortable and the doctor would be right with her. She sank into a chair. Despite its hard plastic surface and the contours clearly designed as an instrument of torture, she managed to doze off. Her body was rebelling against the loss of rest of recent nights, and snatching back a few minutes of sleep when the opportunity presented itself.

The next thing she knew she felt a hand on her shoulder. It seemed gentle enough, but insistent as well, and when she opened her eyes she saw the massive janitor standing over her. She hadn't seen him since their strange conversation about computer languages, when she'd handed him the pages from her notebook.

His usual expression of diffident uncertainty was gone today. The man was positively beaming.

"I was hoping you'd be here," he said. "I didn't know how to get in touch with you." He paused, waiting for a reply, but Jennifer merely waited for him to go on. "You asked me to run that binary material through the computer."

Nodding eagerly, Jennifer signed, *What did it say?*

"I don't know yet," Robert conceded. "I mean, I don't know all of it. But I do know this." He leaned over her, casting a look up and down the corridor as if he were afraid of spies. "It's a message."

Jennifer looked up at him, amazed.

The nurse rose at her station and looked around, ready to call the next patient. Jennifer thought Dr. Leiberman might be ready for her, but until she heard the rest of what the janitor had to say, she wasn't ready for Dr. Leiberman. She rose and took the man by one massive, gentle hand and led him down the corridor, away from the nurse's station.

Puzzled, the janitor demanded to know where they were going.

Jennifer ignored the question. She towed him along behind her, like a child tugging a compliant adult on some secret errand. She halted, the big man close behind her, at a door marked with the international symbol for women. She shoved the door open, took a quick peek to assure herself that the room was unoccupied, and pulled him in behind her. She reached past him and snapped the lock on the door. Now no one could burst in on them.

The man looked around in a state of near-panic. "Um . . . why are we in here?"

Jennifer signed her reply. *We have to keep this secret from them.*

"Secret from *them?*" he echoed aloud. "Who are *they?* What do we have to hide from them? Why do *we* have to hide?"

Jennifer leaned forward conspiratorially. She lowered her voice to a near-whisper. "I have to be careful, they think I'm crazy."

"No, you're not," he protested. "Believe me, this—this is the best thing that could happen to anybody. All my life I've wanted something like this to happen to me. I've dreamed about this. You could be receiving messages from another world."

A year ago, before she'd had her implant, before she'd started hearing the voices, before she'd seen her images of the swollen, seething sun, she would have thought by now that the janitor was the crazy one. But not now.

Not now.

Tell me, she signed.

For a long moment Robert stood, gathering his thoughts. "Um, okay, there isn't much more to tell.

Except that the first part of the transmission—the first part of the coding you gave me, on those notebook sheets—is like a Rosetta Stone. Like—"

He looked around, as if he expected to find something that would help him to demonstrate a difficult concept. There was nothing there, so he relied on words. "There's a string of prime numbers that shows it's a signal, then a series of equations that basically say everything coming next is in base ten arithmetic."

He looked at her. Either she didn't comprehend or she wasn't interested. He said, "This doesn't mean anything to you, does it?"

Never mind that, she signed impatiently, *tell me what the message says!*

"Well, that's the point," he told her. He seemed to be pleading for her to understand. "It's only the beginning, that's what I'm saying. But it's definitely from somebody who's trying to use mathematics as the basis for a common language. The first part of the message is trying to teach us how to read the rest of it, you see? Now who would have to send that kind of, kind of reading instructions, before they got to what they were really trying to tell us?"

Jennifer shrugged.

"Anybody on earth, even using a different language," he resumed, "even from a whole different culture—they wouldn't be *that* different, don't you see? It has to be aliens from another planet. After all these years, after all the phony reports and hoaxes and publicity stunts and—no, I know it for sure, this is the real thing at last!"

He waited for a reply but she only shrugged.

"You gave me the how-to-read-this part," he went on, "now I'm ready for the message itself. You've got to give me the rest of it."

She shook her head, then spoke aloud. "It stopped."

He stood there silently, looking like the not-very-bright, hulking menial worker he had appeared at their first meeting. After a little while he said, "Really?"

She nodded.

He said, "Well, if it starts up again, use this." He reached into a pocket of his worker's outfit and pulled out a small, flat, plastic device. He held it toward her. He worked a tiny latch and the thing opened, revealing a tiny keyboard and a miniature monitor screen. He turned the gadget end-to and removed a memory card.

"See? It'll hold pages and pages. You won't have to do all that writing, just tap out your ones and zeroes and X's. And *I* won't have to transcribe all your writing, I can input directly from the card into my computer."

At first suspiciously, then with growing enthusiasm, Jennifer turned the gadget over, studying it from every angle, finally trying out the little keyboard. With evident satisfaction she finally accepted the device. She folded down the lid and slipped it into her pocket.

To the big man, she signed a question, *What job did you have before?*

His diffident expression came back, more overwhelming than ever. For a moment Jennifer was sorry that she'd asked. If it was going to be this painful for her strange friend, maybe she didn't need to know his background. But something didn't fit right. This man was a computer scientist. Why was he working as a janitor? He could decode a message from an alien race, yet he pushed a mop for a living.

"Would you believe me if I told you I used to work for NASA?" he said. "I did. Years ago. Just after college. I wasn't anybody important or anything, just part of the team. I did some research programming, and some mission tech support. I liked it a lot, but. . . ." He stopped and stood there, hanging his head.

Jennifer positioned herself where he couldn't help seeing her hands. She signed, *Why aren't you still there?*

He swung his head from side to side, the way Allison did when she didn't want the food she was offered. He mumbled, "Oh, well, you know, with government budget cuts and staff reductions and such. . . ."

Someone was pounding on the door. The big man stopped talking. He looked embarrassed. There he was in the ladies' room. He shouted, "Just a minute. I'm cleaning. Try one floor down, thank you."

Jennifer smiled. He could still think fast. He'd thought his way out of an embarrassing moment. To her, the janitor said softly, "Now I'm gonna get fired."

After a moment they heard footsteps receding outside the bathroom.

Something about their narrow escape, like school children sharing a prank and getting away with it, gave Jennifer a sense of communion and friendship with this huge, unusual man. She realized that they'd never been introduced. She'd thought of him simply as the big janitor, not even knowing his name; he probably didn't know hers either.

"Jennifer," she said, pointing to herself.

"Robert," he replied.

They shook hands.

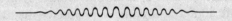

After seeing Leiberman, Jennifer stopped at the pharmacy she used for aspirins and toothpaste, then at the supermarket before she returned to the apartment. She found her husband sprawled on his back in the living room, his arms straight above him, holding Allison, swinging her happily back and forth. His face looked as if he was making noisy sound effects and Allison's looked as if she was having the time of her life.

Sam spotted her in the doorway and greeted her with a grin.

She walked into the kitchen and lowered a heavy bag of groceries on the counter. She turned and saw her husband, on his feet now, carefully placing their baby in her jumper seat in the living room.

He followed Jennifer into the kitchen and watched her unloading groceries. When he caught her eye he asked, "What'd Leiberman have to say?"

Jennifer shrugged. She took a clear amber plastic bottle out of her grocery bag and shook it. Even from this distance, Sam could read the label. Moroxydol.

He could make out Jennifer's name typed on the label, and Dr. Leiberman's, and a few words about dosage.

"He gave you a prescription," Sam said. "He must think they're the right thing." When she didn't reply he resumed, "Did you try one yet? They make you feel any better? You look better."

Jennifer smiled at him. She looked at the label. "Sounds like a new laundry product," she said. He nodded encouragingly. She opened the bottle and shook a tablet into the palm of her hand. She poured a glass of water and popped the tablet into her mouth and followed it with a mouthful of water.

Sam returned her smile. He looked at his wristwatch, then at the big clock as if to check for accuracy. He seemed to reach a conclusion. "Maybe I could put in a few hours at work, and still be back in time for supper. Allison is fed, she seems pretty happy. You be okay in the house?"

She nodded. Things were getting back to normal.

"You sure?" Sam asked. "I don't want to push you, go too fast."

She smiled again and gestured at him, as if she were sweeping dust out of the room with her hands.

"Great." He nodded happily. "Ally's clean, too, I changed her. And we saw two soaps and a game show." Then suddenly he was serious. He reached toward her. "I want you to know, hon, I just want you to be okay. Whatever that means, whatever that takes."

She nodded her understanding, and they embraced. Sam walked from the kitchen, headed for the hall closet where she knew his suit jacket hung. Even a modern businessman had to wear the old three-piece uniform. Then she turned to the sink and leaned over and spit out the tablet. She ran the water to make sure that it was gone.

She sat and watched her baby, and after a while when it was time for Ally's nap, Jennifer put her in her crib and sang to her, trying all the while to imagine what singing sounded like, until her daughter fell asleep. Then she turned away and started back toward the living room.

Sam was gone, Allison was napping, and Jennifer felt that this was the time for some peace for her. But instead she felt a too-familiar stabbing pain in her head. And it was more intense than ever. She gritted her teeth and fought back tears. She crossed the room like a swimmer crawling through waves of agony. A table lamp crashed to the floor. She ignored it, struggling to reach her purse.

The wall clock caught her attention. It read 3:10.

She tore her eyes away from the clock and concentrated on opening her purse. The simplest task was endlessly difficult, but she persisted. She managed to retrieve the plastic gadget that Robert had given her. She managed to open the lid and studied the keyboard. She was no computer professional, but in this day and age it was the rare person who couldn't at least operate a keyboard.

This device was like a miniature computer all itself, she realized, with its own built-in keyboard and monitor screen. Jennifer didn't even need to switch it on and boot up: a miniature pressure-release switch took care of that when she opened the cover.

She carried the gadget to the overstuffed chair and settled in. Maybe the act of concentrating on the microcomputer drew her attention away from the dreadful pain inside her skull, or maybe something about the act of typing in the ones and zeroes and X's relieved a mental pressure. Whatever it was, she felt herself relaxing, losing her self-awareness in what some of her artier friends called *the creative trance*.

She didn't know how long it took her to "receive" whatever message was coming to her. Maybe it was just seconds of high-speed, high-density transmission that her brain stored and then parceled out to her fingers, releasing the data as fast as she was able to type.

She didn't like to hold those packets of information for long. She was afraid that if she did, she would somehow lose them before she had a chance to enter them on the microcomputer. But she could hold them for at least a few hours at a time. Over the next few days she learned that, and the messages kept coming at strangely regular intervals, one each day in midafternoon and one each night—actually, in the pre-dawn morning—at ten minutes after three.

Each day she would manage to get to the hospital and hand a removable data card to her friend Robert. And each day he exchanged a blank card for the filled one he received from her.

As the days passed and the twice-daily routine of receiving and typing messages, the regular exchange of data cards with the hulking janitor, became part of Jennifer's life, she found herself adapting to her new routine. Before, she had spent her nights with her husband, her days with her hearing-impaired students. She had cared for Allison, exchanged greetings with her accommodating neighbor, shopped for groceries, lived a normal life, managed her roles as career woman, wife, and mother as skillfully as a professional performer would juggle oranges and bowling pins and dinner plates.

Now, she did all those things and something new. Now she received her messages each afternoon and before dawn each morning, typed her data cards, held her surreptitious meetings with Robert.

Until. . . .

Sam and Allison were asleep. Jennifer sat in the half-darkened living room, compulsively tapping at the keyboard of her microcomputer. She still didn't know what the messages meant but by now they were so much a part of her that they seemed like the notes of a great silent symphony playing in her brain. They were the only sounds she had ever heard.

But suddenly something was different. She didn't know what, there was nothing conscious about it, yet she knew that the room had *changed*. She looked up.

Sam was standing there. She could see his face but she had trouble reading his expression. He spoke, and she read his lips. "What are you doing?"

She clicked the microcomputer shut, tried to conceal it, holding it against her clothes and covering it with her hands. She knew it was too late to keep him from seeing it, but still she felt that she had to get it out of his sight.

She said, "I couldn't sleep. I didn't want to wake you."

"I thought you were with Ally," he replied. "But—" He pointed. "What's that? Where did you get it?"

If only she'd had a little warning, she could have slipped the tiny computer between the cushion and the arm of the chair. But he'd caught her and he'd seen it.

I bought it, she signed.

He held his hand toward her, demandingly. "Let me see it?"

She shook her head. She was not a child, she was a grown woman and she was not answerable to anyone, including her husband.

"Why not?" he demanded.

Then, after a pause, when she refused to answer, he said, "Jen—are the voices coming back?" His manner changed from angry and demanding to loving and sympathetic. "Because if they are, we need to tell Dr. Leiberman. He needs to know that. He may increase your medication."

Jennifer put her hands over the microcomputer, protecting it from her husband. It was hers, and it was important, and she would not let him take it from her.

There was a moment of tense silence, then she said, very clearly, "No."

Sam said, "You know, I have to go to Chicago for a couple of days. But I'll cancel if you need me here."

She leaped out of the easy chair and flew into his arms. She turned her face up and kissed him on the mouth. After a startled moment, he returned the kiss. When they finally separated, he asked, "What was that for?"

Jennifer looked into his eyes and made sure that he was looking into hers. She wanted him to be sure of her. She knew that she was sane, she knew that she was in control of herself and that she loved her husband, and she needed him to know that, too. Emphasizing every syllable, she said, "Sam, believe in me."

He looked into her eyes. She could read him, she'd always been able to read him. She knew that he did believe her. He said, "Come back to bed, Jen."

And she did.

Still, she had to maintain routine. Until this mystery was solved, until Robert was able to tell her what the ones and zeroes and X's meant, if ever anyone could tell her that, she had to maintain routine.

She sat in the waiting room at the hospital. She had an appointment with Leiberman, and as usual he was running late.

Jennifer scanned the patients waiting for their appointments. One older woman in a peculiarly mismatched outfit sat and muttered to herself. Jennifer tried to avoid making eye-contact with the woman.

Clearly she was a troubled soul, and Jennifer wished her the best, but in her present state she couldn't get entangled with this person's delusions.

But it didn't work. The woman reached for Jennifer and shook her arm. She spoke and Jennifer read her overly made-up lips. "You can hear them, can't you?"

Jennifer shook her head and signed to the woman, *I can't. . . .*

"Yes, you can," the woman insisted. "You can hear them, I can always tell when someone else can hear them." She glared at Jennifer. "You know what I'm talking about . . . *the voices!*"

Jennifer paled. The woman was delusional, while Jennifer knew that she *really* heard them, that *her* voices were real!

Or were they?

How close was sanity to madness?

"Hah! Got your attention, didn't I?" the woman resumed. "Be careful. Sometimes when you're sure it's the voice of God, it's really the devil himself!"

Jennifer was beginning to be frightened of this woman. Clearly she was seriously ill, hearing voices that weren't there while Jennifer only heard voices that were there. Or—

Robert was there. Her friend Robert! And he was waving frantically to get her attention. He was normally so quiet, so diffident . . . She had never seen him so excited. She managed to escape from the bizarre woman and hurry after Robert, into the corridor.

She read Robert's lips as warned her, "I wouldn't talk with that woman if I were you. She really is— you know—crazy."

Jennifer didn't know whether to laugh or to cry with relief. She signed, *What have you got?*

"I don't know what I've got, Jennifer."

She looked at him, puzzled.

"But I've sure got a lot of it," he told her.

Then show me!

"I'll need a lot of room to spread it all out."

Without another word spoken or signed, Jennifer took him by the hand and led him toward a sign. In illuminated green letters it read, EXIT.

Robert followed obediently, happy to be with his new friend and happy to be sharing this intriguing puzzle with her. "As long as it's not the bathroom," he managed.

With Robert beside her, Jennifer drove home. She parked and they took the elevator to Jennifer's floor. She unlocked the front door and opened it. At the end of the short corridor Mrs. Henderson was sitting in the living room, knitting in front of the TV.

She looked up. "Jennifer, you're back." She blinked, looked at the hulking Robert. Unsure of herself now, she managed, "Oh, hello."

Jennifer asked, "Is the baby asleep?"

"She went down for her nap a little early today. We had such a nice walk in the park, but she was tired out." She shifted her gaze from Jennifer to Robert. "Have we met before?"

"I don't know." He tilted his head. "Maybe at the hospital."

"Oh, you work at the hospital. I see. Well, then," she lowered her voice conspiratorially, "I'll just get out of your hair."

She put her knitting in an embroidered carry-sack and clicked off the television. She slipped around Jennifer and Robert, waving, then made her way toward the door. She pulled it shut behind her, giving Jennifer one more brief, appraising glance before it closed.

Robert said, "Is your husband at work?"

Jennifer answered with a single word, "Chicago."

The excited, confident Robert of less than an hour earlier was slipping back into his diffident, uncertain manner. He grunted something that might have been, "Oh," then nervously said, "I need a bare wall and some thumbtacks."

Jennifer scanned the room, then went to the couch that stood against the longest wall of the room. She stood at one end and nodded to Robert, then toward the opposite end of the couch.

After a moment of uncertainty he said, "Oh, okay, I gotcha." He lifted his end of the couch as if he were a child rearranging the furniture in a doll's house, then swapped places with Jennifer and moved her end of the couch with equal ease.

He fumbled in his clothing, them produced a sheaf of computer printouts. While Jennifer stood across the room, staring in amazement, he arranged the sheets on the wall, fixing each page in place with a thumbtack. Jennifer couldn't even tell how he knew which sheet went where; there must be something in the printout itself that told him that.

When he finished, he crossed the room and stood beside Jennifer. Her expression was one of baffled incomprehension as she studied the sheets. His was

one of massive satisfaction. He said, "That's everything so far."

Jennifer looked at Robert, trying to understand
what the printouts could possibly mean. She got
nothing from his expression, so she returned to the
pages themselves. Row on row, they covered the
entire wall. Thousands—no, hundreds of thousands—of ones and zeroes and X's.

What did they mean?

Jennifer blinked, squinted her eyes, cocked her
head. A gasp escaped her lips and she turned and
looked up at her giant friend. She smiled at him and
he smiled back.

Robert said, "Can you find Waldo?"

She ran from the living room, into the makeshift
study where she and Sam kept a desk and filing cabinet and took turns tending to the trivial tasks of running a household. She tugged at the top desk drawer,
rummaged around until she came up with a pair of
plastic cylinders topped by black plastic caps.

Back in the living room she removed the plastic
cap from one cylinder to expose a broad felt tip. She
nodded to Robert, then crossed the room and carefully placed the felt marker at an X on one of the
printout sheets. She ran a line from it, to another X,
and then to another. In seconds she had picked up
speed and was playing a bizarre adult version of con-
nect-the-dots.

When she ran out of breath, still shaking with
excitement, she handed the second marker to Robert
and he continued the task.

At last they capped the markers, crossed the room and stood side by side, gazing at the results of their work.

On the opposite wall, outlined boldly in black dye on white paper, were three standing figures. One was a nude man, holding his hand upraised in sign of greeting. The second was a nude woman, holding her hand upraised. And the third was something that gave every subtle sign of being an intelligent, self-aware creature, but that definitely was not a human being.

It had six limbs. It stood upright on two legs, it had two arms, and it had two intermediate limbs. Jennifer imagined that it could run on all fours, if the necessity arose, and that it could travel at immense speed. Or it could stand upright like a man, as it appeared in the portrait, and use four of its limbs as arms.

Now, three of its arms hung at its sides, relaxed. The fourth was upraised in the same gesture of greeting. The hand wasn't quite a human hand; there were six digits, and the fingers and thumb—or thumbs— were arranged oddly. But it was unquestionably a hand.

Robert looked from the wall to Jennifer, back to the wall and back to Jennifer again. He said, "They want us to know what they look like."

Four arms? Jennifer signed.

"Why not? They evolved on a different planet, there's no reason they should be quadrupeds."

You mean—we finally met the little green men, only they're giant—what would the word be—hexapods?

"I don't know. I guess they're giants—if the pictures are to scale. And green—?" He laughed. "Why not? The picture isn't in color, they could just as well be green as any other color."

Jennifer shook her head. Aloud, she said, "What's all this about, Robert?"

"You know what I think?" The fire of excitement was back in his eyes now. "I think it's a set of instructions!"

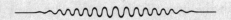

Sam called every day from Chicago. The business trip was going well. If anything, too well. The customer wanted him to stay on and work on new applications. The home office was delighted to have him stay on and book more orders for the company. The only trouble was, he wanted to be home with his "two girls," Jennifer and Allison.

Jennifer assured him that she and Allison were fine. Mrs. Henderson watched the baby and cared for her needs while Jennifer was at work, or at the hospital checking in with Leiberman. She missed him and wanted him to come home, but he had his career and she encouraged him to stay in Chicago as long as he was needed there.

She didn't tell him that Allison was with Mrs. Henderson right now. Jennifer and Robert were working frantically on their project, and the babysitter was providing the care and attention that Allison needed.

Something was growing in the living room. It was a thing of metal and glass and silicon and plastic rather than protoplasm and protein and hemoglobin, but it grew like an organism, tended by its two care-givers, Jennifer and Robert.

They had a manual that they used to build the thing, a manual that Jennifer had downloaded from her voices, that Robert had run through his desktop computing system and printed out in reasonably understandable English. In fact, it was a better man-ual than the ones that had come with some of the high-tech gadgets that Jennifer and Sam had brought home from electronics stores.

Robert lifted a part in one hand, held the manual in his other, and tried to figure out the next step in their construction project. He hadn't felt like this since he was nine years old and his favorite uncle gave him an Erector set.

He looked from the manual to the metallic part and grunted. "So, this is the compressor for the gas plasma." He turned the part over and looked at it from the other side, comparing it to a diagram in the manual. "Oh, I see," he exclaimed.

Jennifer looked over his shoulder at the manual, read a few lines and picked up another part.

Robert said, "Last time I tried to follow a set of instructions this complicated, I was a kid and it was Christmas morning."

Jennifer grinned at the notion of this hulking giant of a man as a little boy in pajamas, standing in front of a Christmas tree, his mouth open and his eyes wide with joy and astonishment.

Behind Robert, at the end of the apartment's short entry corridor, Jennifer saw the front door open. Only someone with a key could open the door, and that almost certainly meant Sam.

He stood in the doorway, peering into the living room, gaping.

Jennifer leaped to her feet and ran to him, eager to tell him everything that had happened in his absence. She was filled with joy, but Sam held her at arm's length, an angry storm-cloud shadowing his features.

"Where's Ally?" he demanded.

Shocked by his attitude, Jennifer signed her answer. *She's with Mrs. Henderson.*

Sam strode into the living room. Robert's fascination with the device that he and Jennifer had constructed gave way to his usual diffidence.

"I'm—we—sorry about the mess. We had to work here, you see, so Jennifer could be near the baby."

Sam gave Robert a steely look. "You're the one who told Mrs. Henderson you worked at the hospital."

"That's right," Robert nodded.

Sam's voice rose in anger. *"You're the damned janitor!"* He dragged air deep into his lungs, barely containing his fury. "Look, fellow, I don't know what you're trying to get out of this, I don't know what you want. . . ."

He turned his gaze toward his wife, then back to Robert. "But Jennifer is very ill right now, you're taking advantage of a very fragile and very vulnerable woman."

"No," Robert shook his head. "No, she's not ill. I can prove it to you."

Jennifer had watched the exchange between Sam and Robert. Now she grabbed Sam's arm and forced him to look at her. She signed, and this time her fingers danced not a ballet of beauty and grace but an adagio of angry energy.

Sam pulled back from her. "All right," he gasped, "I'm listening. What—"

"Robert knows more about this than I do, Sam. He decoded the messages. He—" She turned. "Robert, you better explain to Sam."

Robert's eyes darted left and right, as if he was looking for a way out of the confrontation. But he managed to control himself. He gave it a try.

"Uh, okay, uh, you know about the binary, right?"

Sam said, "No, I don't. What binary is that?"

"That's binary code. All you have to do is look it up yourself and you'll see, *Jennifer* wrote all this down." He pointed to the sheets still tacked to the apartment wall, and to the thick manuals made up of reams of computer printout.

"She wrote it down," he repeated, "not me. All I did was run it through the computer and print it out." He gestured to the wall where the makeshift mural of man, woman, and alien stood silently over-seeing the construction project.

"See, she was writing X's too, and at first, I just ignored them. I thought they were—what we call, uh,—null characters, you see? But when we put the whole thing together, Jennifer realized that they were a palimpsest."

"A what?" Sam demanded angrily.

"Uh—it's a message concealed inside another message. Look." He pointed at the images. "The man and woman are a perfect copy of what we sent out on Pioneer 10. We sent that image of *us,* and they're sending it back with an image of *them.*"

Sam looked at the drawings. He didn't dispute Robert's statements, but one look at his expression showed that he was far from convinced.

Robert gave it another try.

"Okay, I know that Pioneer couldn't be anywhere near another advanced civilization yet. I mean, the distances—interstellar distances—it's just *out there* somewhere, it couldn't be anywhere near another solar system at ordinary speeds. But it left our solar system back in the seventies, and once it disappeared we don't know what happened to it. If it went through a wormhole, or encountered a quantum singularity—"

To Sam Winter this was a lot of technobabble gobbledygook. He cut to the quick:

"Why doesn't NASA know about this? Why isn't the government doing something? If we're getting messages from these—these six-armed Martian monsters. . . ." He stopped and waited for an answer.

"We talked to them." Robert gestured at Jennifer for confirmation. "We talked to JPL and NASA, I have old friends there you know, but we couldn't get anywhere. Either they know about this, it's some kind of cover-up—"

"Sure," Sam interrupted, "just like the UFOs they have stashed all over the country and alien spacemen in the morgue. Come on, buster, you've got to do better than that."

"Well, then," Robert replied, "it might be Jennifer's implant."

Sam's eyes opened wide. "Jennifer's *implant?*"

"She—she told me about it, and it's basically an electronic receiver, isn't it? It was supposed to pick up sound waves but somehow the circuit didn't do its job, isn't that right? Isn't it possible that it's picking up some kind of electronic transmission instead? Some kind of, of, sub-ether carrier wave, or—"

"Oh, absolutely," Sam sneered. He shook his head, then circled the unfinished devices that Robert and Jennifer had been building. He bent over an unopened box of parts and tugged at the envelope containing the bill of lading. Attached to it was a list of charges. His head snapped up.

"Nine hundred dollars? On *our* credit card? Jennifer, what in the world are you doing—buying toys for your friend here?"

Jennifer shook her head, stymied by her husband's rage.

Robert took a hesitating step forward. "That's a capacitor in that box. Some of the parts we can find, others we've had to try and make from these instructions." When he saw that his words were having no effect on Sam he pushed on. "Look, Mr. Winter, the aliens want us to build a laser, it's really special, it's different from anything that anybody has ever tried before."

"Get out of my house," Sam hissed at the giant.

"No." Robert held his hands in front of his face as if he expected to be struck. "I just haven't explained it right. See, Jennifer's voices, they were messages, they—"

"Out! Get out!" Sam's face had turned a bright red; Robert backed away, one tiny step after another. But he wasn't fast enough to escape the raging Sam. The smaller man grasped Robert's shirt collar as if he were about to lift him bodily off the floor.

"I've got a degree in astrophysics," the big man cried, "you have to believe me."

"I don't have to believe a thing!" Sam hurled the bigger man away from him. Robert stumbled to the door, fumbled with the knob and latch like a desperate child, then managed to swing the door open and fled.

Jennifer had watched the incident, horror-stricken. Maybe she was wrong to keep Sam in the dark about Robert and the decoded messages, about their alien manual and their desperate construction project. But he'd seemed so convinced that her voices were nothing but hallucinations, she'd feared that telling him all this would only convince him that she really was psychotic.

But once he'd seen the alien "portrait" and the laser, if only he'd listened to Robert's explanation, he might have been won over to Jennifer's side. He would have believed in her again, and that would have been so important. Instead, he'd acted like a bully. Like a school-yard tough, throwing his weight around, dominating another boy who was bigger but who just didn't understand how to face down a bully and stand up for his rights.

For the first time in her marriage, she was ashamed of her husband. She loved him as much as ever, but instead of feeling proud of him, she was let down and disappointed. She wiped away a tear and turned and walked from the room.

Sam followed her. "Jennifer . . . Jennifer, wait!" But her back was toward him and she did not hear.

She walked past their bed and opened the closet and pulled out a suitcase. She flung it angrily onto the bed and opened it, started throwing clothing inside. She felt Sam grab her arm but she snatched it away from him and went on with her work.

But this time he was the bigger one, and he forced her to look at him. He said, "If I'm angry, it's because you lied to me."

"*You* lied," she shouted back. "When you said you believed me, you lied! *You!*"

She slammed down the lid of the suitcase. It might contain an oddly matched assortment of garments but she was not going to stop and sort things out. She hefted it from the bed and stormed out of the room.

Her husband ran ahead and tried to talk her out of leaving, stammering and trying to sign at the same time. She looked left and right, not at him. He did not try to block her path or hold her back. In a moment she was past him and out of the apartment, leaving him alone and ashamed.

That wasn't the end of it. She hailed a cab and communicated her needs to the driver. He extorted a big fare and a bigger tip, but he was willing to take the job. He went back upstairs with her and helped her haul the equipment to the elevator and manhandle it into the cab. Sam sat in the living room and glared, but didn't try to stop them. The extra parts and documentation went into the trunk along with Jennifer's single suitcase. The laser filled the back seat and Jennifer rode in front with the cabbie.

"Jeez, lady, what'd the guy do to you? And what's the machine there, looks like a cross between a searchlight and a cannon."

"Something like that," Jennifer told him.

"I mean, who was that guy, your husband? He been beatin' on you? You oughtta call the cops, not just run out, you know, they got laws nowadays about that."

Jennifer shook her head, fighting back her tears. "He didn't hit me. I just have to go." She didn't know if they were tears of grief or of rage.

Robert must have seen the cab approach. He was at the entrance of the converted warehouse when it pulled up, and he helped the cabbie move all their equipment and Jennifer's suitcase inside the building. He asked, "Are you sure about doing this?" But even before Jennifer could say yes, the cab had pulled away.

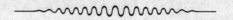

They were farther along than they'd realized. For days on end they worked, taking breaks for naps and snacks, then returning to their task. At times they combined their efforts. At others, they came to places in the job that called for the close concentration of a single worker; then they spelled each other, one resting while the other pushed ahead.

What had happened to their respective jobs, neither knew, but they could guess. Jennifer's principal knew that she had been seeing a psychiatrist and taking medication for her condition. He would have called the apartment, spoken with Sam, and had Jennifer placed on medical leave. As for Robert's supervisor at the hospital—well, menial labor, casual labor . . . they came and went. You could always hire another floor-swamper and towel-changer.

But now the laser was nearly finished. It was so close to completion, Robert felt himself tingling with excitement. He held a klystron tube, carefully attaching it to delicate leads.

Jennifer had been napping on an old thrift-store couch. She opened her eyes and watched Robert. She must have made some small sound because he looked over his shoulder and said, "I thought I should let you sleep."

"I had a good rest."

"You needed it. When that last batch of binary came in—did you know you were typing for twelve hours straight?" The messages came in twelve-hour bursts, but Jennifer usually alternated between copying them down and enduring the pain to rest her hands and her mind.

"I wasn't counting." She managed a tired smile and a little joke. She sat up, then made her way to the sink to rub some water on her face. When she turned back, Robert said, "It was great stuff. I ran it through the computer and got a ton of data out of it. It'll take me all day to make sense of it, but maybe that's the end."

She nodded. "Maybe." Then she said, "That thing you said at the apartment—"

"What thing was that?"

"About Pioneer. I'm younger than you, you know."

"I know," he laughed.

"I don't remember much about the seventies. I don't remember that Pioneer."

Robert turned a typing chair backwards and sat down, leaning his arms against its back. His face grew soft, as if he was retreating into memory.

"We had such hopes then. We thought—" He shook himself back to the present. "Pioneer 10 was an unmanned space probe. It was programmed to head out along the plane of the ecliptic—"

He caught the look in her face and backed up.

"That's like, um, a flat pie-plate, and all the planets revolve in roughly the same plane. Pioneer went far out, toward the outermost planets, then took a turn out of the plane and headed off into unknown space. They put messages on it, just in case anybody ever found it. There were diagrams of humans. That's what those pictures were. And samples of our science and our art. There were even sound recordings. I wonder what a Bach organ fugue or a Chuck Berry guitar riff would sound like to those aliens."

"I wonder myself," Jennifer said. Then a rictus of pain distorted her features. She staggered toward Robert, grimacing with agony.

"It's still coming, isn't it?" he asked. "And it's more painful than ever, isn't it?"

She nodded, gasping, unable even to speak. She grabbed his outstretched hand and clutched it for support.

Slowly, Robert nodded. "I know why now. I understand it at last. They're getting closer." He led her to a chair and helped her to sit down. She clutched the edge of the computer table to steady herself while he worked for a few minutes at the keyboard. The pain was still there, but its intensity had peaked and she found she could tolerate it, look past it at what Robert was trying to show her.

At last the image on the monitor screen cleared. It was the earth, as if seen from space, gracefully and majestically turning beneath them, like a giant, beautiful marble slowly rolling through emptiness.

Robert said, "The earth revolves on its axis every twenty-four hours, right? So, every twelve hours we come in alignment with—with some point in space, don't you see? Like the tides, any point on earth comes in line with the moon every twelve hours, once when it's closest and once when it's farthest? Don't you see? It's not exactly like that because the moon is revolving around the earth, too, but it's the same idea. Your signals are coming from—someplace out there, and every twelve hours you come in line with the source, and that's when they hit."

Jennifer let out a little sound, somewhere between a gasp and a moan. She gestured, then signed to Robert that the fierce pain of the message had receded, then leveled off as a throbbing, powerful headache.

"Sure," he tried to sound encouraging, "I have an economy bottle of aspirin in the cupboard above the sink. Wait here, I'll get you some."

"No," she said. Then she signed, *You stay at this. I'll go get it myself.* She didn't want to sit still while he went for the pain-killer. Even if it didn't save any time, she wanted to be moving and doing something to help herself, not waiting for another to help her.

She stumbled into the kitchen and found the cupboard he'd mentioned. She opened it and looked inside for the aspirin. It was there all right, but there was another bottle beside it, a clear amber plastic prescription bottle.

She reached for the green aspirin bottle but her hand hesitated. She looked over her shoulder like a guilty schoolgirl, then turned back, lifted the clear amber bottle and read the label.

Moroxydol.

Shocked, she turned the bottle in her hand. Moroxydol, and the patient's name, Robert Vitale. Funny, she'd known him only as Robert, almost as if he had no other name. Robert Vitale, and a physician's name—not one that she recognized—and the dosage instructions, one tablet, twice a day, same as her own.

Moroxydol. Not a washday product. The antipsychotic drug that Dr. Leiberman had prescribed for her. She'd thrown the pills away, carefully disposing of them one by one so the number left in the bottle would always tally if Sam checked up on her. But Robert was taking the same drug. And he had no one living with him to keep track. If he had one of the familiar clear amber bottles of Moroxydol in his cupboard, that meant he was really taking the drug.

That he really needed the drug.

Everything he'd ever told her about himself came roaring down on her like a freight train on a midnight grade. His story had been unbelievable from the start. How could she have believed him?

A degree in astrophysics?

A former computer scientist for NASA?

Old friends at the space agency and at the Jet Propulsion Lab? A computer setup here in his home?

And all of this, while he trudged through his days pushing a broom or steering a floor polisher in the hospital? A man who built super lasers to communicate with aliens in his spare time, when he wasn't busy installing new rolls of toilet paper in the ladies' rest room?

He *was* crazy.

And she must have been crazy, too. Sam was right. Dr. Leiberman was right. She had to be crazy to believe in this lunatic! She felt tears welling in her eyes; she wiped them away and stood there shaking.

Slowly she reached up, the clear amber bottle in her hand. She put it back on the shelf. Robert mustn't know that she had found it. He mustn't know that *she* knew what he really was.

She turned around.

He stood close to her, watching her. He raised his hand and she cringed but he only waved it as if to show her that he meant no harm.

"Unless I take those twice a day, I start to hear voices too, Jennifer."

She was too frightened to speak. She signed, *You never worked at NASA. You made it all up. And I believed you.*

"I'm not making it up." He shook his head. "I really did work at NASA. That was before my first psychotic episode." He shrugged his massive shoulders. "I worked on Pioneer, that's how come I remember it so well. I was just a kid, just out of college, and I had a bright future ahead of me. I thought I was going to be a great scientist. I knew astrophysics, I knew computer programming, I knew a little engineering. I was the fair-haired boy." He ran his fingers through his short, thinning hair, grinning wryly.

"You know, they used to think it was all emotional," he said, suddenly serious. "They thought crazy people were that way because of something their father said to them or their mother did to them or because they didn't get to nurse enough when they were babies—but they know better now. It's a chemical imbalance in the brain, that's all. A lot of mental illness is. Schizophrenia is. If they can track it down, find out what's wrong, they can help a lot of people. It worked for me. I'm really all right now. Really."

She stood there watching him.

"As long as I take my medication," he added.

For some reason that reminded Jennifer of her headache. She stared at the two bottles, the clear amber prescription bottle of Moroxydol and the green glass bottle of aspirin. She held the Moroxydol toward Robert. He pointed to his wristwatch. It wasn't time for his medication. She lifted the bottle and placed it carefully in the cupboard.

"I was acting pretty bizarre," Robert went on. "They didn't understand what was wrong. Neither did I. So when I messed up they fired me, they didn't know it was my— Things got bad for a while. I started living on the street. I lived like that for a year. It's all like a nightmare now, sometimes I can hardly remember it and sometimes I can't remember it all. Then I wound up in jail. I don't even know what I did, you know? Isn't that weird? Maybe I'll look into it sometime. I could write a program that would break into the database at the courthouse, that would be easy, and find out what I did."

Jennifer stood watching him.

"But somebody from the mission and somebody from the public defender's office came over and got me transferred from the jailhouse to the hospital." He smiled at her. His smile *looked* sane enough. "And they figured it out and got me on meds and now I'm really okay."

He took a deep breath, then he finished his story.

"That's how I got the job, working as a janitor. I haven't been there very long. I just need to get my life back together, and then I can get a good job again, I can do the work I'm qualified to do. But for now—Jennifer, you have to understand this—I heard voices, but they were never real. I know that now. They were just in my head. But your voices, Jennifer, I know, *your voices are real.*"

She looked at him and he looked back. He stepped aside so she could get past him. "If you want to leave, Jennifer, I'll understand."

She peered into his eyes, and after a moment she signed to him. She told him that she was not going to leave. He was the one who should leave the kitchen, and go back to the workroom, and get on with their project.

He said, "Okay, okay, I'm working, I'm working." And there was a big smile on his face.

Once he walked away, she studied the green bottle of aspirin. Her headache had come back, but it wasn't the monstrous, agonizing headache it had been. It was just an ordinary headache. She opened the lid on the green bottle and shook out a couple of aspirins. She swallowed them with some water and followed him back toward the computer.

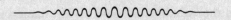

Sam Winter held Allison against his shoulder. He was trying to comfort her, rock her to sleep. She was clean and fed and in her own familiar home. Her father was holding her. She should have been happy, but she wasn't. Sam Winter knew what was wrong. Allison was too young to speak in words, but she told him with her whimpers and her body language. She was looking for her mother.

So was Sam. He'd tried Jennifer's school, he'd tried both Dr. Madison and Dr. Leiberman. He'd grilled Mrs. Henderson, their regular baby-sitter, but she couldn't help. He'd tried Jennifer's parents' house over and over, until he realized that they were even more frantic than he was—and no less ignorant.

A hundred times he walked to the medicine cabinet and stared at Jennifer's bottle of Moroxydol. Without it, she might start hearing her voices again. And once that happened, there might be more symptoms; *anything* could happen. Worst of all, she might be hanging out with that lunatic janitor from the hospital, Robert.

Sam Winter didn't even know Robert's last name. He'd gone to the hospital to look for the man, only to learn that he hadn't shown up for days. "Abandoned his job," was the way they put it. Bureaucratese. He hadn't exactly quit and he hadn't exactly been fired. He'd "abandoned his job" and been dropped from the rolls. His final check would be mailed out at the end of the pay-cycle.

But they wouldn't tell Sam his last name and they wouldn't tell him where he lived. Right of privacy. Federal regulations. Didn't want Robert to turn around and sue them for violating his rights.

Sam tried Dr. Madison again. Dr. Madison barely knew what he was talking about. The janitor? Sorry, but who notices janitors? A big fellow, must weigh close to three hundred pounds. Short hair, little beard, always shuffles around looking like he'd faint dead away if you said "Boo!" to him.

Sorry. My patients, you know, and my work. Keeping up with the literature, keeping up with the field.

Madison was hopeless.

Then Sam tried Dr. Leiberman.

Bingo!

Robert was a patient of one of Dr. Leiberman's closest pals. Sure, right here in the hospital. In-house care was a benefit of working for the hospital. They discussed their more interesting cases all the time. Robert the janitor was a classic.

No, Dr. Leiberman couldn't tell Sam the man's full name or address or even Robert's doctor's name. Doctor-patient confidentiality was involved. Dr. Leiberman didn't want to get hit with a lawsuit any more than the hospital's personnel department.

But by an odd coincidence he'd recently borrowed Robert's folder from his doctor. Certain similarities to Jennifer's case, and he'd just happened to be studying Robert's case when Sam dropped in to visit. And he might have to attend a staff meeting, leaving the folder right on top of a stack of work, right on top of his desk, while Sam was there.

Oh, there was no need to come back later. He'd only be gone for a few minutes. These staff meetings could drag sometimes, but he knew the agenda today and it was a short one.

When Dr. Leiberman did get back to his office from the meeting, Sam Winter had left. Unsurprised, the doctor took the file folder off his desk and left it for the staff to return to his colleague.

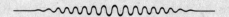

Robert was working at the computer while Jennifer checked the assembled laser against schematics from the alien manual. Robert turned from the monitor and keyboard and caught Jennifer's attention. She laid down the manual and joined him at the worktable where the computer stood.

The monitor screen showed a schematic of some huge device; it looked like a cross between a kite and a giant glider. As the image rotated, Jennifer could see that it was almost two-dimensional. If someone had spread a film of infinitesimal thickness across a lightweight frame. . . .

She couldn't tell the scale. Long rows of numbers ran across the bottom of the screen, but they were meaningless to her. She was an elementary school teacher, not a mathematician. Maybe Robert, if he really was an astrophysicist, could understand them.

Jennifer pointed at the image. She signed, *What is it?*

"It's a light sail." Robert half-turned so that he could see the screen and Jennifer at the same time. "I think it's a monomolecular film, the thinnest form of matter that's theoretically possible." He rubbed his chin. "Unless it's a plasma. That could be even thinner, if there were any way to stabilize it and make it useful."

A film? Jennifer signed.

"So thin that a sheet of paper would be like a pile of mattresses. And it's really big. It has to be a thousand miles across, at least."

Jennifer shook her head, puzzled. *But what is it? What is it for? What does it do?*

"It's never been done," Robert told her. "We tried to design these things when I was at NASA, but they never really got off the ground."

She looked baffled.

"Space-science humor. Sorry." He managed a small grin. Then he got serious again. "If you could make a sail that was big enough and lightweight enough, and if you could get it into space and moving, it could use the solar wind, the light pressure of the sun itself for propulsion. We worked the figures, I even remember some of them. To give the sail a boost—get it started and up to speed—you could use a ground-based laser. It's like the old dream of transmitting electricity without wires. Only we're using light energy instead of current."

And the aliens want us to build one? Jennifer signed.

"No." Robert shook his head. "The aliens *have* built one. They're not just from another planet, they're from another star, someplace . . . someplace. . . ."

Jennifer pointed at the schematic of the light sail on the monitor screen. In the image it was attached to a small cylinder. If the sail was what powered the ship, then that tiny cylinder must be the ship itself. And if a giant spaceship—she only guessed, but somehow it had to be a giant spaceship—looked this small on the screen, then the sail had to be immense. Far beyond anything that anyone could make on earth.

She said, "Why are they standing still?"

"I just stopped the animation on the screen," Robert explained. "This is what's really happening."

He clicked the keyboard and the picture came to life. The giant, distant sun blazed and the ship moved ever so slowly toward the sun. Ever so slowly, yes, but on the scale of the image, it must be hurtling at incredible speed,

"You see?" Robert said. "This is the course they're on." The animation continued. "And they're headed straight for the sun. Something went wrong with their navigation. If we look in the right place, we might even catch a glimpse of their ship as they flash by the earth. And then they'll be gone. Fried to a crisp."

On the screen the image of the ship showed as a tiny black dot against the sun, then disappeared for a moment, then reappeared as a brilliant, flaring firework, and then was gone.

No! Jennifer pointed to the monitor screen, then to the laser they had built, then used sign and speech together in her excitement.

"That's what it's for. That's why they told us how to build this laser. They want us to save them."

Robert turned and studied the laser. "Maybe. This might be enough to deflect them around the sun.

Then they'll pick up energy from the sun and . . . and *slingshot* on, out of the solar system and on to—wherever they're headed. We used that technique at NASA, slingshotting probes from planets to save on propellant. But—the aliens—we'll never know where they went. We'll never meet them. We'll never even get to know who they really are."

We know that already, Jennifer signed. *They're people. They don't look like us but they think and build and travel. Maybe—maybe they even like music. They're people. And if we can do this for them they'll be saved.*

"You're right," Robert assented, "they'll be saved."

Hurry, Jennifer signed, *we have to finish our work!*

Hours later night had fallen over the city. The sky overhead was clear. A million stars and planets and distant galaxies gleamed like brilliant gems against the blackness. Jennifer scanned the sky, wondering if one of those gleaming gems was the alien spaceship.

They had hauled the laser onto the roof of the building in parts and carefully assembled it there, and it stood now, shining in the starlight. Power cables ran from the laser down a staircase into the warehouse. The power draw would not come from any ordinary household circuit, but from the heavy industrial buses left behind by the last tenant.

Robert had bolted the base of the laser to the roof to stabilize it, and stacked heavy sandbags against its legs to absorb vibration.

Jennifer looked away from the sky and studied the laser. To Robert she signed, *Is this right?*

"I hope so," Robert sighed. "This is as good an approximation as we could get to what the instructions said. Remember, they're not just not-human, they're not even from earth. I *think* they meant sandbags. Or as close to that as their experience and, and our shared vocabulary, could tell us. We just have to hope it works."

She signed, *It will.*

Robert looked at Jennifer. Now that they were ready to use the laser, now that they were waiting for the critical moment, he was concerned about her. "How's your head?" he asked. "Any more messages? Any more pain?"

Jennifer signed her answer. There was pain, but this close to the end, she knew she could handle it.

Robert looked at the sky, then down at his watch. "Oh, my God! How could I forget? I'll need a camera. We have to record this—if their ship is visible, we have to capture the image."

He stumbled past Jennifer and down the staircase. Taking two steps at a time, holding onto the ancient handrail for balance, he hurried back to his own apartment and workspace. Moving at top speed he emerged from the stairwell and confronted—*Sam Winter!*

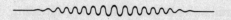

On the roof, Jennifer waited—and waited. She scanned the sky, studying the stars. Which of them was not a star at all, but a tiny, fragile life-raft carry-ing people who had been born beneath another sun? And why had they left their home world, and where were they going? For a moment she squeezed her eyes shut and offered a silent prayer, her fingers moving to send her message to God.

But then—where was Robert? The moment was nearly here, and he'd gone to fetch his camera and he hadn't come back. What could have happened? If he'd fallen in the stairwell and injured himself he might be stranded there, unable to return—and she would never have heard the crash, nor his cries for help.

She started down the stairs after him.

She reached the floor where she knew Robert had gone. She raced across the open space and turned a corner and found her husband and her friend together. Sam had Robert pinned against a wall. Even though Sam was the smaller of the two men, he was full of violent rage, and Robert was a man with no violence in him.

Baffled, the bigger man stood against the wall, taking one smashing blow after another from the smaller man's fists.

And Jennifer could see enough of Sam's bright-red, fury-filled face to read his shouted words: *"Where's my wife? What have you done with her?"*

Robert seemed paralyzed with terror at Sam's astonishing attack. Without raising a hand to defend himself, he gasped, "She's on the roof, I swear. I didn't touch her. She's—they're coming tonight. We have to save them. They're almost here. Right now!"

Sam glared up at Robert's face. He followed the bigger man's eyes, turned and saw his wife. She had witnessed the encounter, had seen him beating Robert mercilessly.

Now she turned and ran away.

He shouted, "*Jennifer!*" but she didn't hear him. She kept on running.

She made it to the stairwell. She had enough of a lead to stop and slam the door shut before continuing up the stairs. She scrambled toward the roof as fast as she could go, knowing that the door had not locked, knowing that her husband would jerk it open and race up the stairs behind her.

She felt a hand on one ankle, then a second. She felt herself pulled back, back down the stairs. She twisted in her captor's grip, found herself confronting the man she had loved and lived with, who was now—she didn't even know. Now, maybe he was her enemy.

He said, "I'm not here to hurt you, sweetheart, I just want to take you home."

Below, in Robert's living and working space, the big man had regained control of himself. He raced after Jennifer and Sam, toward the stairwell. He yelled, "It's time! They're coming!"

He managed to get through the doorway and start up the stairs.

Sam yelled back over his shoulder, "Get away from us!" And, to Jennifer, "I talked to the hospital administrator, I talked to Dr. Leiberman—Jen, this man's crazy, he's schizophrenic, he's been feeding you nothing but lies. This whole thing with aliens and spaceships is his crazy fantasy."

From below, Robert implored, "Jennifer, it's now or never. They'll burn in the sun!"

Still grasping Jennifer with both hands, Sam yelled back at Robert. "Leave us alone! Just get away and leave us alone!"

Jennifer struggled to escape from Sam, to scramble up the stairs and fire the laser before it was too late. Sam put all his attention into holding her back, ignoring Robert, who grabbed him from behind and pulled him away from Jennifer.

For the first time, Robert had directed his strength to his struggle with Sam. He lifted the smaller man bodily, lifted him over his head and flung him at the far wall. Sam struck the bricks with a sickening thump and slid to the stairs. For a moment he lay there, then he moved.

Robert looked up at Jennifer. She was staring at the two men, horrified by the violence they had both displayed. Robert shouted, "Jennifer, *go!*"

Below them, Sam had pushed himself to his knees. He dragged himself a few feet, then stopped. Weakly, he implored Jennifer. "If you love me, Jen, please . . . don't. . . ."

Jennifer looked from one man to the other.

With hideous visions burning in his eyes and his brain, Robert urged her once more. "There's no time, Jennifer. *Go!*"

She turned her back on both men and ran to the top of the stairwell. She flung open the door and climbed onto the roof. She turned back and shut the door behind her. She salvaged a metal rod from the materials she and Robert had used and wedged it into the door frame to keep any pursuer at bay.

With a final glance at her own wristwatch, she flung herself toward the laser. It was pre-aimed, ready to project critical power to the exact point where it was needed, to billow out the alien ship's light sail, to swing the ship those crucial few degrees from its trajectory and send it sweeping safely around the sun and on into the black night of space.

The firing sequence had been programmed into a computerized control panel. Robert had done that, Jennifer had watched him at work. She didn't understand the firing sequence but he had showed her how to initiate it, and that was all she needed to know.

She hit the keys as Robert had taught her, and stood back to watch the flashing indicators check the circuits and then—*fire!*

A narrow beam of light flashed from the laser, blazing into the sky. Jennifer fell back from it, silhouetted against its brilliant intensity. It lasted only a matter of seconds, but to Jennifer Winter it was as if an eternity passed while she stared, fascinated, not at the metal device she had helped to build but along the course of the beam of light.

At its far terminus there appeared briefly the object that the light had been sent to save. It must have been the alien spaceship, but it was nothing like the spaceships Jennifer had seen in motion pictures and television shows and comic strips since she was a girl. And it was nothing like the Apollo rockets or the space shuttles she had seen in news broadcasts and newspaper photographs.

It looked like a giant jellyfish, or better yet a giant beautiful moth. Its wings were huge, its body relatively tiny, but she knew that it must have been large enough to carry its crew and to sustain their lives during a journey of unknown duration, across distances incalculable.

And even in those fleeting moments, she thought she detected a slight movement, a minute alteration in the position and the direction in which the beautiful thing moved.

It swept over her head like a storm-swept cloud in a wintry gale, and she stood watching the beautiful thing as it passed into earth's ken and then out of it again, all in a matter of seconds. High above the planet, the light sail caught the first rays of dawn and billowed out, and the ship adjusted course and increased its velocity.

Jennifer raised a hand and signed, *Good-bye, friends.* She knew the aliens could not see her, could never know her gesture, and she wept, uncertain of why.

The stairwell behind Jennifer was surmounted by a translucent panel, a skylight long since coated with falling dust and condensing emissions. Even so, as Robert stared up at it, he could see the diffused colors as the laser fired and the alien ship responded first to the light of the laser, and then of the dawn.

He stood there whispering incoherent syllables of awe, and joy, and relief. He understood what he was seeing.

Then he felt a sudden impact on the side of his neck, and a crunching sound as a rabbit punch descended from behind him. He toppled, revolving, and saw Sam's half-maddened face, before he crumpled to the stairs.

Sam raced up the stairs and crashed against the door at the top of the stairwell. It yielded a fraction of an inch and stopped. He braced himself against the handrail and kicked at it, again and again.

Jennifer clutched her head with her hands as a final wave of sickening pain passed through her. Then it was gone. She nearly collapsed at the passing assault, but she kept her eyes fixed on the alien ship. The laser clicked off, responding to its automated controls. The alien ship faded from sight.

She turned slowly away, in time to see the door to the stairwell burst open as the bracing rod gouged a trough in the roofing and rolled to a halt. She saw her husband staring at her like a madman. Then he raced toward her.

She looked away, hoping for a final glimpse of the alien ship, and as she did so she saw Sam follow her lead and turn his face to the sky.

Only the stars blazed back at them.

Behind Sam, the battered Robert stepped onto the roof. He, too, turned to the sky. But Jennifer knew that Robert, unlike Sam, knew what to look for, and where to look for it. He shook his head sadly and looked back at Jennifer.

Through her tears, Jennifer told him, "We saved them. Robert, we saved them!"

"We did?" he echoed. "The laser worked?"

She nodded.

"You saw them?" he asked.

She nodded again, unable to speak or to sign.

Again Robert looked up. Somewhere inside of him, he may have hoped to find a trace, a glimmer of the sail in the rapidly brightening sky. But he saw nothing, as he must have known would be the case.

He said, "Now they're gone."

Sam watched the bigger man. Whatever madness had come upon Robert, he deduced, had receded at least for now. And at least for now the sometime janitor was a harmless, gentle giant. Sam stood facing Jennifer. He wanted to be kind, he wanted her to know that he loved her and that he wanted to believe her.

But what had he seen?

Nothing but a useless, oversized flashlight. The product of the shared delusion of two mentally ill individuals. A pile of high-tech junk paid for with Sam's own credit card!

He said, "I'm happy for you, sweetheart. But we can't stay here. We have to go home now. Your friend will be all right by himself. And little Allison misses her mom."

She did not move.

"Jennifer?"

She looked at him as if at a stranger. He thought she was crazy. He still thought that. He still thought that everything she and Robert had done, was meaningless. Then she looked at the sky again. There was no light sail there, no laser beam. Only the stars, fading and fading and finally disappearing in the growing light of day.

But she had seen the ship. She knew what she had done. She whispered, not to Sam, but Sam heard her whisper. "We saved them."

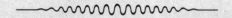

RICHARD A. LUPOFF is the author of several dozen novels and nearly a hundred short stories. His most recent book, Before . . . 12:01 . . . and After, *is a collection of short stories covering more than forty years of his career. The title story of the collection has been the basis of several motion pictures. Lupoff has written for a widely varied range of publications, including* Ellery Queen's Mystery Magazine, The Magazine of Fantasy and Science Fiction, Murderous Intent, Heavy Metal, *and* Hardboiled. *His most recent novels are* The Cover Girl Killer *and* The Silver Chariot Killer.